The C++ Project

Marcos Tewfiq holds bachelor's degrees in Electronics Engineering (from Instituto Tecnológico de Aeronáutica - ITA, in Brazil), Law, and Economics (both from the Pontifical Catholic University of Rio Grande do Sul - PUCRS, in Brazil). It is worth mentioning some online courses related to the subject of this book: C++ Nanodegree Program, by Udacity; Professional Certificate in C Programming with Linux, by Dartmouth College and Institut Mines-Télécom, on edX; 2.086x: Computational Thinking for Modeling and Simulation, by MITx, on edX. Although indirectly related to the book, deserve to be mentioned these courses on Coursera: Fundamentals of Computing Specialization, by Rice University; Intro to Robotics Specialization, by the University of Pennsylvania; Cybersecurity Specialization, by the University of Maryland.

[This book is not affiliated with, authorized, sponsored, or approved by the institutions mentioned. The specific online courses cited above have not conferred University grades, course credits, or degrees, but certificates of completion.]

The C++ Project

A companion for learning the C++ programming language

Second Edition

Marcos Tewfiq

Sao Paulo

Beelectronic

2021

The C++ Project
A companion for learning the C++ programming language

Second Edition

Any suggestions are welcome. Please contact support@beelectronic.com.

ISBN-13: 978-65-991627-5-6   [Revised in June 2022.]

Dados Internacionais de Catalogação na Publicação (CIP)
(Câmara Brasileira do Livro, SP, Brasil)

```
Tewfiq, Marcos
   The C++ Project : A companion for learning the C++
programming language / Marcos Tewfiq. -- 2. ed. --
Piracicaba : Beelectronic, 2021.

   ISBN 978-65-991627-5-6

   1. Algoritmos de computadores 2. C++ (Linguagem de
programação de computador) 3. Ciência da computação -
Estudo e ensino 4. Programação (Computadores
eletrônicos) 5. Softwares aplicativos -
Desenvolvimento 6. Tecnologia I. Título.
```

21-63070   CDD-005.133

Índices para catálogo sistemático:

1. C++ : Aplicação em algoritmos : Computadores :
   Processamento de dados 005.133

Aline Graziele Benitez - Bibliotecária - CRB-1/3129

To my parents,

family, friends, teachers, and readers,

this book is dedicated.

Axe, and it shalbe geuen you:
Seke, and ye shall fynde:
knocke, and it shalbe opened vnto you.

Matthew 7:7
Myles Coverdale Bible, 1535

Contents

Introduction

Programming a computer to simulate some physical system, and doing experiments with it, certainly will increase our knowledge of physics and the universe that surrounds us without the costs and difficulties of the real experiments. This book will illustrate a simulation of this kind meanwhile presenting some useful hints and concepts about programing in the C++ language.

One of the greatest tools to understand the world is the computer, but almost nobody knows what it really is or how to program one. With that machine, we can try to make simulations or play our microcosms, making an incommensurable number of experiments with virtually no risk.

With computers, we can expand and exercise our creativity. All we need to do is to write a new equation or a new program. Working on our understanding of physics and mathematics, for example, by getting perceptions about the random processes, and simulating them, can have broad consequences on our understanding of the universe.

As a tool for creativity, this book is a brief introduction to programming using the C++ programming language through its key points. We have illustrated it with a small program, using about 1.800 lines of code. The program allows users to simulate elastic collisions of multiple balls, with up to one hundred balls roughly simulating a gas confined in a cylinder, The Kinetic Theory of Gases and The First Law of Thermodynamics. The same kind of structure can simulate other physics or even social phenomena.

We have made improvements using the same program structure, adding the capability of inelastic collisions and implementing the restitution coefficient. In addition, through the processing of Newton's Law of Gravitation, we have created gravitational simulations, which besides being oversimplified, are especially useful.

In this second edition, we present another new simulation, of virus propagation, with an also remarkably simple model based on popular knowledge. Each ball (representing a computer) is infected when it collides with another and stays in this state during a period, transmitting to the others through the collisions. Lastly, the ball goes to the recovered state when it is not able to transmit anymore. Using these premises, we simulate with two different ball speeds, but it is possible to simulate using different intermediate state periods and ball speeds.

We have considered you know nothing about programming but have access to a computer with Linux (Ubuntu) or Windows operating system and know its basic commands. However, this is not a complete course! The goal is to be a reference, a companion, or an inspiration for learning. The computer is not for computer scientists only. It is like a piano at your desk, with countless online courses and resources for you to learn how to play!

This work intends to be a good complement because we will use a program to illustrate the programming language, giving a more practical and general approach. You will see that there is an absurd amount of information to learn in computer science, and having a reference or a practical work is useful to mark our progress and consolidate it.

Nevertheless, we think this same program structure can be adapted to applications in Social Sciences, especially in Economics, and maybe also in Arts and Biology. This is because the program is, in fact, several mini-programs running simultaneously, independently. This kind of autonomy, provided by the junction of object-oriented language and concurrent computing, in conjunction with the power of C++ language, especially the high speed in the execution of the programs, brings possibilities only limited by the programmer's imagination.

Underlying Physics

The program has two simulation modes. In the standard, the program uses these equations for the movement of balls and the piston:

$$m0*v0i + m1*v1i = m0*v0f + m1*v1f \quad \text{(Conservation of Linear Momentum)}$$

$$Ec0i + Ec1i = Ec0f + Ec1f \quad \text{(Conservation of Kinetic Energy)}$$

In the "gas" mode, the piston moves according to the force exerted on it by the balls. The program uses these equations for the piston:

$$F*(tf - ti) = m0*(v0i - v0f) \quad m0: \text{ball mass} \quad \text{(Linear Momentum-Impulse Theorem)}$$

$$F = m1*a \quad m1: \text{piston mass} \quad \text{(Newton's Second Law)}$$

In the gravitational simulations, the program applies Newton's Law of Gravitation and also the equivalence between the gravitational force and the centripetal force:

$$F = \frac{GMm}{r^2} \quad \text{(Newton's Law of Gravitation)}$$

$$F = m\frac{v^2}{r} \quad \text{(Centripetal Force)}$$

We can see that the book helps teach physics through observing and thinking about the program output and by the exercise of programming new simulations.

Output Screenshots

See in Figure 1 (below) the screenshot of one possibility of output from the case of multi-ball collision remembering a gas confined in a cylinder. It is possible to simulate an elevation of the system energy by applying some "heat" at the bottom (use the left key). The bottom color will change to light red, and the minimum ball velocity will increase by some value.

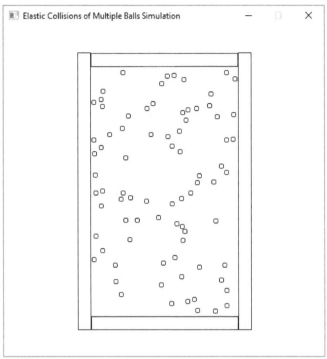

Figure 1 – Screenshot of simulation: 80 balls colliding.

Screenshots from the other simulations are in the respective chapters, but the overall aspect is a little different. The size of the cylinder, its shape (it can become a square), the thickness of the walls, and the radius and number of the balls (depending upon the computer machine processing speed) all can be adjusted for the simulations.

Key concepts

We start by explaining some major concepts of the area in focus, which is a computer programming language in the field of computer science.

There is a universe of information in this area. Almost all the material that we have read has brought huge quantities of information. Sometimes, direct contact with this enormous quantity is not a good start and even makes some people give up learning.

In our experience, we have noted that only a fraction of the knowledge is enough to make very expressive works but is common in books and internet published material much more than that, without filtering about what is fundamental. So, we have selected some key concepts.

We recommend you search through the free encyclopedias on the internet for the fundamental concepts below and write some in a sketch. After that, we will illustrate the concepts with small pieces of code, when applicable.

Please, search for **computer**; **program**; **source code**; **memory** (computer memory); **memory address**; **memory value**; **variable** (in mathematics); **variable** (in computer programming); **symbolic name**.

A computer is a machine that executes a program, which is a sequence of operations. The operations can include the storage of values, for example, a word, where each value is a letter, or a text, a big sequence of data. The operations may also be calculations. Nevertheless, this kind of definition is poor in terms of the real meaning and importance of computers.

When we see the computer at the hardware level, it is possible to understand that the computer is only hardware. Besides the keyboard, where we enter data, that data will go inside hardware. We need to think about this.

We have a machine, or hardware, where we enter data using a keyboard, for example. Before we have entered the data, we have a machine, a physical one. After we have entered the data, we still have a machine. Its mass and its size did not change.

Think about your computer when you type a text. Disconnect it from the internet, disconnect from the wireless. Think about the computer before you enter some text. Enter some text and think about what happened. Is it the same machine?

The answer, you could say, would be yes, it is the same. Where did the data you have typed go? It is inside the machine; you can see it on the screen! Answer the question: how is it possible to be the same machine if now the data is inside it?

We can think that a computer is a reconfigurable machine. The data, or the program, or anything that happens, make the machine change. In fact, a computer can simulate vehicles, airplanes, and even other computers. This is possible because we can reconfigure and reconstruct part of the hardware with the data we entered. We can enter a program that will reconfigure the machine to be an airplane, not to really fly like one, but to simulate one.

The other side of this kind of understanding is that computers can be a great resource to comprehend the world because we can try to reconfigure the machine to simulate some phenomenon, and with this, improve our understanding. It is worth saying that the computers and the process of trying to simulate the physical world, translating this physical world to the physical reconfigurable hardware, are the actual procedure to knowledge in almost all knowledgeable matters. Please, see more in the references [1]. Even in a very modest way, the program we have brought in this book is an example.

Besides the program that we can put to work on the machine, our program needs another one that will run in parallel with it, helping with some tasks, serving as an interface between our code and the physical hardware, and doing several other things that keep the computer working. That is the "**operating system**" program. It starts running just after we turn on the machine.

There are important differences between operating systems. Please, search about the differences, including the privacy and security configurations.

Please, also search for more concepts (in computer science): **input/output**; **scope**; **function**; **return statement**; **return value**.

The concept of "**function**" in computer science is different from that of mathematics. Inside a program, a function is a piece that we isolate from the rest to make the program easier to read and understand so it will be easier to build a greater program.

There is a limit to our ability to coordinate several things at the same time or to get a full understanding of many different things in movement. When we isolate some tasks in a separate piece of software, which probably will get some data, process it, and return the result, our ability to construct a bigger program increases.

As an airplane when surpassing the sound speed, when we are working on a big program, there will be, at some moment, a strange sensation that it is impossible to understand what is happening if we try to do it in the normal way, trying to get the whole at the same time. When we perceive that we are not able to understand the whole, but the machine works, this means that we have surpassed our maximum capacity! How is this possible?

This is possible because of the "**functions**" and other entity, the "**objects**", which represents an advancement in the same direction.

Please, search for the concepts: **abstraction** and **encapsulation**.

We prefer to think that "**encapsulation**" is the result of the process when we make a function, for example, isolating some part of the software that will perform some tasks. The "**abstraction**" would be the process of isolating things that have attributes in common, such as the commands needed to print a message, to build a function that will print the message.

Now it is time to illustrate the concepts. We begin with reference to the program that illustrates this book. Please, see the source code in **Appendix A**. Each **Appendix A** subtitle is the name of a file. Please, see the "**Ball.cpp**" file, and go to line 467:

```
467    double distanceToPoint(double x1, double y1, double x2, double y2)
468    {
469        double distance;
470
471        distance = sqrt(pow(x1 - x2, 2.0) + pow(y1 - y2, 2.0));
472
473        return distance;
474    }
```

We have the function **distanceToPoint** in the code above. The function will receive as parameters the **x1** and **y1**, **x2** and **y2**, the coordinates of two points. It will calculate the distance and return the value with "double" precision. Search for the **fundamental data types** in C++, especially **int** and **double**.

In line 469, we have the **variable** "distance", and in front, we have its **type** "double". This is the **variable declaration**. It will tell the computer that it needs to reserve a space in its memory, whose name will be "distance" and will contain a value of type "double", which is a decimal type.

Search for **declaration of variables**.

See line 471: it is the **initialization** of the variable. Initialization means that the variable will carry a value, or we will put a value on the memory (whose symbolic name is "distance") after calculating it. We reproduce that line below:

```
distance = sqrt(pow(x1 - x2, 2.0) + pow(y1 - y2, 2.0));
```

The right side, after the equal sign, will calculate the value. The left side is the variable, where it will save the value. The right side is the code for the mathematical formula of the distance between two points (in a two-dimensional plane). Please, compare with the formula:

$$\text{Distance} = \sqrt{(x1 - x2)^2 + (y1 - y2)^2}$$

Search for the function **pow** and the function **sqrt** in the C++ language references. These functions are ready to use, so we do not need to write them. They integrate the program by a language command, at line 7 of **Ball.cpp**:

```
#include <cmath>
```

This **#include** command tells the program to get all the mathematical functions of a **library** of functions called **cmath**, already written for C++, and put them at our disposition if we need to use them inside the program.

Therefore, we have "encapsulated" all the calculations inside the function **distanceToPoint.** If at any other place in the program we want to know the distance between two points in a 2D plane, we just need to "call" for the **distanceToPoint** and inform it (pass as parameters) the coordinates of the points, as we did at this line of code (see line 461):

```
distance = distanceToPoint(x1, y1, x2, y2);
```

When we are calling the **distanceToPoint**, the only thing that we must know is what data it needs to make the calculations. We also need to know the order of the data and the form of how we must pass it. In other words, what we need to know is the **function declaration**, as in the line below:

```
double distanceToPoint(double x1, double y1, double x2, double y2);
```

The function declaration will appear in another place of the code, normally at the beginning. The example above tells us that the function will return (or output) a value in a "double" number and needs four "double" numbers as input (x1, y1, x2, y2). This is also called the **function signature**. As we do not need to know the implementation, nor the code inside the function, we are "abstracting" the calculations.

Together, the concepts of "encapsulation" and "abstraction" are explanations of how it is possible to write programs with about one hundred million lines of code as the modern operating systems.

Now, we will introduce the general notions about how we write software in practice.

The building processes

The core of the computer is its **CPU** or "**central processing unit**". It is responsible for executing the instructions of the program. The language the CPU understands is not the human-readable programing language, like C++, but the "**machine code**". The "**compiler**" is a special program that makes the conversion of the programing language in the machine code. The process has other parts, like joining the pre-compiled libraries with the main program. The entire process receives the name of "**building**" or "**software build**". Please, search for the concepts.

The goal of the building is to make an executable file, a program that the computer or **CPU** can understand because it is written in machine language.

The entire process starts with a text written on a text editor in the programing language that we choose. Then, we "build" the executable by calling the "compiler", and after, the "linker", which will join all the other software needed (all the other "libraries") together with our program. In this building process, we normally use automatic scripts or tools. One example is the **Make** tool. With just one command, this tool "makes" the build process, executing pre-configured instructions (it is like a program) in the **Makefile**.

In our example, we use the **CMake** tool, which is more flexible than the **Make**. The **CMake** will execute the **CMakeLists.txt** file, whose copy is in **Appendix A**.

Another way of doing this is to use the **Integrated Development Environment** or **IDE** tools. Many free tools provide text editors, compilers, linkers, and debuggers, all in one piece, with a graphical interface. Normally, the editors also incorporate code analysis and suggestions for corrections.

With an **IDE**, we just need to write our code and know how to command using the menu options in the graphical interface. The **IDE** makes the software developer task easier, but the graphical interface, with the hundreds of commands and options, is a little intimidating at the beginning. Do not worry. It is perfectly normal.

When we isolate the essential functions of the **IDE**, the commands and ideas we need are few. The main things that we need to know are:

a) the structure of the program and its folders;
b) how to load and save the files (generally at the File menu);
c) how to build the executable (usually at the Build menu) and run the program.

After that, we can also know:

d) how to set some **IDE** options (normally at Tools > Options);
e) how to set specific properties to our program (Project > Properties, for example);
f) how to debug the program (normally at the Debug menu).

Now we will get a brief understanding of the C++ language with illustrations. After that, we will guide you through one C++ simple program using three methods, including the **IDE**.

Special hints

We think that knowing a language means structuring the understanding based upon three pillars: a) the language syntax and semantics; b) the building process or IDE facilities; c) the knowledge of the libraries you are going to use. Therefore, it is not only about the syntax, but the overall difficulty extends to the building, IDE, and libraries.

It is an "ocean of information", which can become extraordinarily complex! We suggest studying just what is necessary as a first approach, not all the details or formats. Remember that computers and programing are at the edge of human knowledge. Programing is to be constantly learning.

When you do not understand something, try to search on the internet and try to do some tests.[1] Do not forget that you have a laboratory of computer science at your hands: the computer. So, do experiments!

When you are stopped at some impossible error, take some distance from the program, and think about it in another place. When you see some error message, try to search for the error in the programing forums. If you are struggling, make a break. When you resume, try to think like a detective. Read the messages carefully and think about them.

When we program a computer, we are trying to tell the machine what to do. Think that this is not a one-way conversation. The machine will try to tell you what is wrong. Try to understand it.

Another key observation is that we can find in all the systems some pieces or concepts that repeat themselves. If we learn in one system, we can likely learn by analogy in another system. For example, all the languages have some general concepts in common, like the concept of variable. Hence, try to find the analog pieces. Please, see more in the references [2].

Sometimes we think that learning the building process, and making the piece of program a reality, is as difficult as learning some programing language. Do not be afraid if you experiment with the same feeling. Things will become more manageable after practicing and surpassing many building error messages.

Not everything that appears to be an error is one. There are model limitations, such as maximum velocities in our example program. Besides, there are limitations in the real world too!

Finally, and particularly important: validate your program! Make several tests, beginning with the simpler and progressing to the broader. In the process, in case of errors, try the debug features, like "breakpoints", and an especially useful, the printing of key variables! Insert some print commands at strategic places (at the beginning of functions, for example) to show the content of variables that you think are important for the analysis.

---

[1] There are a lot of places, but an excellent first reading is the tutorial at www.cplusplus.com/doc/tutorial/

Variables

In mathematics, we can write an equation like

$$a + 1 = 0$$

and solve the equation, obtaining

$$a = -1$$

where "a" is the variable. We can also write

$$-1 = a$$

In C++, we can write

```
int a = -1;
```

Observe the "int" and the semicolon. Each language has its conventions for writing the statements. A statement is like an instruction to the machine. The semicolon tells that we have finished what we are asking it to do.

The example above will tell the computer to reserve a space in memory, whose name will be "a", for storage of an integer, whose value is -1. Therefore, we have a clear analogy with mathematics. However, there are significant differences.

First, that is not an equation; we cannot write

```
a + 1 = 0;
```

Second, what is at the left of the equal sign is quite different, in terms of functionality, from what is on the right. On the left, there is the place where we will store. On the right, it is the value. As a consequence, we cannot write

```
-1 = a;
```

We can also see the address of the variable "a", or in other words, the address where was stored the value -1. This is like the physical location (in a very simplified way of thinking). We just need to put "&" in front of the "a", like "&a". In the code below, "b" will have the address of "a":

```
int a = -1;
int* b;
b = &a;
```

We see that "b" is declared with "int*" instead of "int". This is because "b" will not have the value of "a" but the address of "a". That is the way C++ understands the thing.

Functions

In mathematics, we can write a function like this

$$f(x) = x^2$$

The "x" is the argument or input, and the value "f(x)" or "function" of "x" is the output. In case, the output will be equal to "x^2".

In programing language, we have an analog entity, the "function", which not only can output numbers but also do everything we want, like a box that we put several instructions inside and ask to do all of them.

In C++, we can write:

```
1    double f(double x)
2    {
3        double result = pow(x, 2);
4
5        return result;
6    }
```

The "f" in line 1 is the name of the function. We can use any other we want, except special C++ reserved words, like "int", for example. We cannot start the name with a number. The "double" in front of the "f" is the type of the value that the function will return (or output).

The "x" in line 1 is the "parameter". The "double" in front of the "x" means that we can pass as "x" a value of type "double". This type "double" resembles the set of the real numbers in mathematics but is truncated at some digit, as that type "int" is like the integers but limited to a maximum value.

The statement in line 5 means that the function will "return" or output what is inside the variable "result". The "result" is declared and initialized (with a value) in line 3.

The "pow(x, 2)" means that we call the function "pow", passing the "x" and the exponent "2". The "pow" is a function of C++, already written for programmers to use, that will calculate the exponentiation.

In line 2, we have a delimiter that tells the computer that we have started to write the instructions or statements of the function. Finally, in line 6, we mark the ending of the function.

Observe that before the end of the function, we must "return" something, that is, tell the computer what the output or result will be. It is necessary because we have declared the "double" type before the name of the function, telling the computer that we were planning to return a value of type "double".

Data structures

In "data structures", we can group different variables with different data types. It is like a "fabric" of compound data types.

For example, we can write a data type specially elaborated for saving the point coordinates at a two-dimensional plane:

```
1   struct point {
2       int x;
3       int y;
4   };
5
6   point p1;
7
8   p1.x = 0;
9   p1.y = 0;
```

The "point" is the name of the new data type, which has the "x" and "y" variables of type "int" as "members". The "point" is not a variable but is the name of a new type of variable. It is like a template or a fabric of variables.

In continuation, in line 6, we are telling the computer to create a new variable of type "point" with the name "p1". After that, we initialize the variable "p1" in its "x" member (line 8) and in its "y" member (line 9).

Instead of referencing "p1" as a "variable", we can call it an "object". This is a broader concept because the "p1" is also more than the "variable".

As the "point" above is like a template, we can write

```
10  point p2, p3;
11
12  p2.x = 1;
13  p2.y = 1;
14
15  p3 = { 2, 2 };
```

We have declared more two points, "p2" and "p3" (line 10) and initialized them with x = 1 (line 12) and y = 1 (line 13), and x = 2, y = 2 (line 15). We have used, in lines 12 and 13 and in line 15, two different but equivalent syntax.

The "point" is the "fabric" of the "p1", "p2", and "p3" "objects". They are all data of type "point".

12

Classes

The "class" is a data structure that can also contain functions. This is especially useful because we can put together the data and operations that we want to make on them, all inside the same place.

As the data structure, the "class" is also a model, a "fabric" of "objects". Now, the objects are more complex because they can have data and functions joined. For example, what operations would we like to do with points on a plane?

One possibility is to make the points move by some distance. We can write a function that will add to the actual coordinates the "x" and "y" displacements we need for the move.

Another possibility is to calculate the distance between two points. For that, we can construct a class to save the point coordinates and make the class carry a function for calculating the distance between one point and the other. We can write:

```
1   class Point {
2       private:
3           double _x;
4           double _y;
5       public:
6           Point(double x, double y) { _x = x; _y = y; }
7           double getX() { return _x; }
8           double getY() { return _y; }
9           void move(double moveX, double moveY)
10          {
11              _x = _x + moveX;
12              _y = _y + moveY;
13          }
14          double distance(Point other)
15          {
16              double result;
17              result = sqrt(pow(_x - other.getX(), 2) + pow(_y - other.getY(), 2));
18              return result;
19          }
20  };
21
22  Point p1 = { 0, 0 };
23  Point p2 = { 3, 4 };
24
25  double d1 = p1.distance(p2);
26
27  p1.move(3, 1);
28
29  double d2 = p1.distance(p2);
30
31  std::cout << "Distance d1 is " << d1 << std::endl;
32  std::cout << "Distance d2 is " << d2 << std::endl;
```

In the program above, we declare the class "Point", starting at line 1 and finishing at line 20. We observe that it resembles a struct but has many differences.

By convention, we use the first letter of the name as uppercase. We named it "Point" instead of "point".

In lines 2 and 5, we also see the words "private" and "public". This means that there are two different regions in the code, one that can be accessed only by the class itself and the other that is "public" and can be accessed outside the class. In other words, if we declare p1 as an object of type Point, we cannot use p1.x to set or get the coordinate "x" of p1. Instead, we need to use some function already written inside the class to do that. This is a safeguard against unwanted changes in the data.

By convention, we use an underscore at the beginning of the variable name, in the case of private members, to signalize that we cannot use the point to access the variable. For example, if we try, we need to write p1._x in the example above. However, this will remind us that "_x" (line 3) is a private member, and we cannot access it in this way.

In lines 3 and 4, we have the "private" variable members. In lines 6 through 19, we have "public" members. In line 6, we have a "constructor", which is like a special function to initialize the data members. In lines 7 and 8, we have two functions, each one with the role of returning a private data member, the "_x" by the "getX" and the "_y" by the "getY" functions. In lines 9 through 13, we have the "move" function. Finally, in lines 14 through 19, we have the "distance" function.

In line 22, we declare and initialize the point "p1". This statement automatically calls the "constructor" at line 6, passing the arguments (0, 0), and the constructor will set the "_x" with "0" and "_y" with "0", initializing the coordinates of the point. In line 23, we declare and initialize the point "p2", with coordinates {3, 4}.

In line 17, we use another C++ function, the "sqrt", which calculates the square root.

Line 25 is particularly important because we will use the advantages of the class declaration.

The output on the screen (lines 31 and 32) will be:

```
Distance d1 is 5
Distance d2 is 3
```

One necessary step before using a program is to make some tests. We can make simple ones by entering inputs for known output results and comparing them with the output of the program.

In the example, a right triangle with sides of lengths 3 and 4 will result in a hypotenuse with length 5. This is equal to the output distance "d1", so the program is correct.

In line 27, we call the "move" function of "p1". Observe that to call a function inside the object "p1", we use the "p1.move". We pass the arguments (3, 1), and the function will add them to the actual x and y coordinates of "p1".

A significant difference between functions and functions inside classes is that the former has a more general scope and objective, whereas the latter has the objective to access and change the member variables of the object to which it belongs.

The object, as an instance of a class, for example, the object "p1", as an instance of class "Point", is like a mini-program. It has variables and functions, also called "methods", like a small program. This makes it easier to get concepts from the real world to the computer, and it is how things happen: at the same time. The real world can be reproduced by designing software to process in parallel.

When we move the point "p1" at {0,0} by distance 3 in "x" (represented by "_x") and 1 in "y" (represented by "_y"), it will be on {3,1}, which is below point "p2" at {3,4}, so, distant 3.0 units. This is equal to the output distance "d2". Hence the program is correct.

In line 25, we call the function "distance". Observe that we make this by writing "p1.distance". This means that we call the "distance" that is built inside the "p1" object. Therefore, this "distance" can access the "_x" and "_y" of the "p1" directly (because another function member can access the private variable members, as it is "internal" access). We pass the "p2" as an argument to "p1.distance". To access the "p2" coordinates, the "distance" must call the "p2.getX" and "p2.getY" (see line 17).

By convention, we usually write the "**signatures**" of the member functions or methods (the name, return type, and parameters) in a file with the extension "h" (means "**header**" files). The **implementations** of the member functions or methods (the statements) are in another file with the extension "**cpp**" (means c plus-plus, or source code files). Usually, we can also include some implementation in the header files if that implementation has one line of code. Another file, also with extension "cpp", will have the core of the program, where it starts. See the files below.

File "Point.h":

```
1    #include <cmath>
2
3    class Point {
4    private:
5        double _x;
6        double _y;
7    public:
8        Point(double x, double y) { _x = x; _y = y; }
9        double getX() { return _x; }
10       double getY() { return _y; }
11       void move(double moveX, double moveY);
12       double distance(Point other);
13   };
```

File "Point.cpp":

```cpp
1   #include "Point.h"
2
3   void Point::move(double moveX, double moveY)
4   {
5       _x = _x + moveX;
6       _y = _y + moveY;
7   }
8
9   double Point::distance(Point other)
10  {
11      double result;
12      result = sqrt(pow(_x - other.getX(), 2) + pow(_y - other.getY(), 2));
13      return result;
14  }
```

File "Main.cpp":

```cpp
1   #include <iostream>
2   #include "Point.h"
3
4   int main()
5   {
6
7       Point p1 = { 0, 0 };
8       Point p2 = { 3, 4 };
9
10      double d1 = p1.distance(p2);
11
12      p1.move(3, 1);
13
14      double d2 = p1.distance(p2);
15
16      std::cout << "Distance d1 is " << d1 << std::endl;
17      std::cout << "Distance d2 is " << d2 << std::endl;
18
19      return 0;
20
21  }
```

This file separation is necessary to make the programs more readable and organized. Note that we only need to know the declarations at "Point.h" to use the class and its member functions "distance" and "move". In other words, we only need to know the "interfaces". If we want to know the implementations of "distance" and "move", then we can study the "Point.cpp".

Look at the file "Main.cpp". We see the function "main", with return value "int", and no parameters. In line 19, we see the function returning "0". This is a convention of the language, which will start to run the program at the function "main". It is the "entry point" for the program.

Observe inside the "main", lines 7 and 8. We are using the class Point to create two objects, p1 and p2. We do not see, in this file, the class Point, but we see a reference to it in line 2. The "include" command makes the file "Point.h" part of the program. If the "Point.h" has all the signatures of its members, then we do not need to do anything more. The compiler will find the "Point.cpp" and make the connections.

Now, try to see in Appendix A which of the files are headers and which are source codes.

Another two more concepts are necessary for the basic understanding of classes. They are "**inheritance**" and "**polymorphism**".

With "inheritance", classes can be built by taking another class as a base class and adding other variables and functions to that. Then, the derived class "inherits" from the base class.

With "polymorphism", we can write the same function, but with variations in its signature, as the number of parameters. The program will automatically call the function that better fits the arguments. Please, search for these concepts.

Control flow

The flow of a program can include instructions to check for conditions, to execute some command only if some condition has been achieved, or to repeat the execution of instructions until the program reaches some condition.

For example, print on the screen the message if the value of the variable "a" is equal to "1". If not, print another message:

```
if (a == 1) {
    std::cout << "The condition a = 1 was reached." << std::endl;
}
else {
    std::cout << "The condition a = 1 was not reached." << std::endl;
}
```

For example, increment "a" until it reaches a = 10:

```
int a = 0;
while (a < 10) {
    a = a + 1;
}
```

Instead of the "while", we can use the "for". For example, starting from "0", increment "a" and print on screen until it reaches a = 10 (print between "0" and "9"):

```
for (int a = 0; a < 10; a++) {
    std::cout << "a = " << a << std::endl;
}
```

We can also use "switch" to evaluate multiple conditions:

```
switch (a) {
    case 1:
        std::cout << "The condition a = 1 was reached." << std::endl;
        break;
    case 2:
        std::cout << "The condition a = 2 was reached." << std::endl;
        break;
    default:
        std::cout << "Unknown condition." << std::endl;
        break;
}
```

Practice 1

Now it is time to practice the real programming, with two examples. First, we will build a simple program in one file to write "Hello World" on the screen. Then, we will write a three-file program to calculate the distance between two points. We will use tools in the Ubuntu (Linux) and in the Windows operating systems.

In Ubuntu (Linux), we just need to create a folder, with a name, for example, "HelloWorld". Inside that, please create a file and assign some name, for example, "HelloWorld.cpp" (with extension "cpp" by convention), and put the content (using an editor, like the "gedit"):

```
1    #include <iostream>
2
3    int main()
4    {
5        std::cout << "Hello World!" << std::endl;
6        return 0;
7    }
```

In line 1, we "include" (tell the compiler to get the content of) the library (collection of functions and classes) "iostream", which has the object "std::cout", which is used to send data to the screen, with the "<<" operator. In line 5, we send the data to the screen.

In line 3, we declare the "main" function without arguments and specify that it will return a value of type "int". In line 6, we return "0" to attend the declaration.

In line 4, we mark the beginning of the code block with "{". In line 7, we mark the end with "}".

Now we need to make the executable file that will have the machine code for the computer to be able to run it. To obtain that, we need to build it using the tools that come with Linux. We can compile and link (the entire building process) with one command:

```
$g++ HelloWorld.cpp -o HelloWorld
```

After that, we will have an executable file named "HelloWorld". We just need to run:

```
$./HelloWorld
```

Practice 2

Download and install "Microsoft Visual Studio"[2], which is an IDE and will have all you need to write and build the program. Use the "Community" version. At some point, you will need to define what language and tools you will use with the IDE because it is able to work with several languages. Please, choose the C++ desktop development. With the Visual Studio opened, you can set this through the menu Tools > Get Tools and Features.

Then, open the Visual Studio and create an empty C++ project. If you have already opened it, you can create an empty project by using the menu File > New > Project.

Reset the windows layout by going to menu Window > Reset Window Layout. This ensures that we will have the same layout.

Observe on the right of the main window of Visual Studio that we have the "Solution Explorer". This window shows the project files. If you pass the mouse through the upper icons, you will see an icon with the name "Switch Views". It is because we have two possible views: a friendlier one, which shows the places "Header Files", "Resource Files", and "Source Files", and another not-so-easy view that shows the actual folder structure. The latter shows a complex folder structure. We will use the former.

The general rule is that you will see a tree, where the tree nodes have names, and at its ends, we have another node or a leaf, which is a file.

Right-click above the "Source Files" and select Add > New Item. Then, select "C++ File(.cpp)" and change the default name that appears at the bottom of this window to the name HelloWorld.cpp. This will make appear a file (a leaf) under the "Resource Files" (tree) node.

On the left of the main window, see the editor window with the name HelloWorld.cpp. If not, just click on HelloWorld.cpp at the Solution Explorer to open the editor window. Now, click inside the HelloWorld.cpp window and type the program.

For running the program, go to menu Debug > Start Debugging. This will compile, link, and run the program, in the "debug" mode. This will open the tools used for debugging the program and a system window that will show the output ("Hello World!") of the program.

Observe that the Visual Studio has several menus and submenus. The IDE configuration, which we can access by Tools > Options, seems to have more than a hundred options. The project configuration is in Project > [project name] Properties. Nevertheless, we do not need to know everything. It is possible to do our job with just some commands.

Two important configurations menu to note are the Solution Configurations and the Solution Platforms. Just pass the mouse over the icons that are below the main menu bar. In the standard view, you will see the "Debug" and the "x86" selected. We can configure the "Debug" and "Release" versions of the program as we choose the platform (x86, x64, and others).

---

[2] This book is neither affiliated with, nor authorized, sponsored, or approved by Microsoft Corporation.

Practice 3

Now we will use another tool, the CMake in Linux, to build a program with three files. They are:

Main.cpp:

```
1    #include <iostream>
2    #include <iomanip>
3    #include "Point.h"
4
5    int main()
6    {
7        double x1, y1, x2, y2;
8
9        std::cout << "Enter the point 1 coordinates, separated by a space" << std::endl;
10       std::cin >> x1 >> y1;
11
12       std::cout << "Point 1 will be at (" << std::fixed << std::setprecision(2) << x1
13           << "," << y1 << ")" << std::endl;
14
15       std::cout << "Enter the point 2 coordinates, separated by a space" << std::endl;
16       std::cin >> x2 >> y2;
17
18       std::cout << "Point 2 will be at (" << x2
19           << "," << y2 << ")" << std::endl;
20
21       Point p1 = { x1, y1 };
22       Point p2 = { x2, y2 };
23
24       double d1 = p1.distance(p2);
25
26       std::cout << "The distance between points is " << d1 << std::endl;
27
28       return 0;
29   }
```

Point.h:

```
1    #include <cmath>
2
3    class Point {
4    private:
5        double _x;
6        double _y;
7    public:
8        Point(double x, double y) { _x = x; _y = y; }
9        double getX() { return _x; }
10       double getY() { return _y; }
11       double distance(Point other);
12   };
```

Point.cpp:

```
1  #include "Point.h"
2
3  double Point::distance(Point other)
4  {
5      double result;
6      result = sqrt(pow(_x - other.getX(), 2) + pow(_y - other.getY(), 2));
7      return result;
8  }
```

Please, create a directory named "PointsDistance". Inside, create two sub directories, named "src" and "build". Put the files Point.h, Point.cpp and Main.cpp into the "src". Create a blank text file named CMakeLists.txt (with uppercase M) and put it at the root of the "PointsDistance" directory.

The folder structure will be, at this time:

```
<PointsDistance>
    CMakeLists.txt
    <src>
        Point.h
        Point.cpp
        Main.cpp
    <build>
```

Open the CmakeLists.txt and write:

```
1  cmake_minimum_required (VERSION 3.5)
2
3  add_definitions(-std=c++17)
4  set(CXX_FLAGS, "-Wall")
5  set(CMAKE_CXX_FLAGS, "${CXX_FLAGS}")
6
7  project(PointsDistance)
8
9  add_executable(PointsDistance "src/Main.cpp" "src/Point.cpp")
```

Change to the <build> directory and call the "cmake" passing the root directory:

```
$cd build
$cmake ..
```

It will call the "cmake" on the directory "PointsDistance". Then, the CMake will process the CMakeLists.txt and output a "Makefile" inside the <build>, which is the actual working directory (remember that you are using the <build> as the working directory). List the content of <build> and see the Makefile. Now, just call "make":

22

```
$make
```

Please, read the messages. You will see "Building CXX object ...". After, you will see "Linking CXX executable ...". This is the Make tool working to build the executable.

The folder structure will be, at this time:

```
<PointsDistance>
    CMakeLists.txt
    <src>
        Point.h
        Point.cpp
        Main.cpp
    <build>
        CmakeCache.txt
        <CmakeFiles>
            (many files and directories …)
        cmake_install.cmake
        Makefile
        PointsDistance
```

At the end of the building process, you will have the "PointsDistance" executable file inside the <build>. As you already are inside the <build>, just run the program by calling "PointsDistance":

```
$./PointsDistance
```

Let us see how the errors will appear with this system. Open the Main.cpp (inside the <src>) and write the word "double" at line 7, with a typo as "ddouble". Therefore, we are simulating an error. Save the file and close it. Change to the <build> and call the "make" again. You do not need to call the "cmake". Just call the "make":

```
$make
```

See the error messages. The first error message will show the error in line 7, in the "ddouble". You can see that after this error, the compiler does not recognize the x1, y1, x2, and y2. All the other errors are a consequence of the first one.

Variables 2

The curly brackets limit a block of code "{" and "}", marking its beginning and end. If we declare a variable inside a block, it will be visible or will be accessible inside that block. It is worth searching about the "**tree structure**" concept. See the example below:

```
1   #include <iostream>
2
3   int main()
4   {
5       int a = 1;
6       {
7           int b = 2;
8           std::cout << "a = " << a << std::endl;
9           std::cout << "b = " << b << std::endl;
10      }
11      std::cout << "a = " << a << std::endl;
12  }
```

We can see one block in lines 6-10 nested inside another block in lines 4-12. The variable "a" is visible through lines 5-12, and the variable "b" is visible through lines 7-10. The variable "b" is not visible at line 11 because its block has ended at line 10. Because of that, the code below will not compile. The compiler will show an error, like "b is undefined".

```
1   #include <iostream>
2
3   int main()
4   {
5       int a = 1;
6       {
7           int b = 2;
8           std::cout << "a = " << a << std::endl;
9           std::cout << "b = " << b << std::endl;
10      }
11      std::cout << "a = " << a << std::endl;
12      std::cout << "b = " << b << std::endl; // Error
13  }
```

The error occurs because we are trying to access the variable "b" at line 12, which is out of its scope. Try the code below.

```
1    #include <iostream>
2
3    int main()
4    {
5        int a = 1;
6        int b = 3;
7        {
8            int b = 2;
9            std::cout << "a = " << a << std::endl;
10           std::cout << "b = " << b << std::endl;
11       }
12       std::cout << "a = " << a << std::endl;
13       std::cout << "b = " << b << std::endl;
14   }
```

Line 13 will print "3" instead of "2" because it is accessing the "b" of the outer block (lines 4-14), which was declared in line 6.

This visibility of the variable is also the "**scope**" of the variable. We can see it appearing in several circumstances, for example, in functions or flow control statements.

A variable that can be seen everywhere in the program has a "**global**" scope. A variable that we can access only inside a function, or a block of code nested inside the "main", has a "**local**" scope (local to that block of code).

Another related concept is the "**namespace**". With a "namespace", we can distinguish between variables with global scope, even if the variables have the same name. The "namespace" will transform the global scope into separated scopes, giving each its own "namespace scope".

For example, see lines 12 and 13 of the code above. The "std::cout" means that we are using the "std" namespace, which is the scope of the Standard C++ Library (collection of classes and functions part of C++). Search for "C++ Standard Library". Inside the "std", we are using the "cout", an object that represents the standard output "stream" (the terminal).

The concept of scope also applies to objects and functions. For example, a function declared inside a class will be only visible by the related object. If it is "public", we can call it, but only using the object name. See the line 16 of the code below:

```
1    #include <iostream>
2
3    class Test
4    {
5    public:
6        void myFunction() {
7            std::cout << "Print from myFunction" << std::endl;
8        }
9    };
10
```

```
11
12    int main()
13    {
14        Test test;
15
16        test.myFunction();
17
18        return 0;
19    }
```

Another important type of variable is the "vector". It is a "container" that can store a collection of other objects or elements. It is like the "array", but while the "array" has a fixed size, the "vector" (of the standard library) can change and has several methods to modify it. Therefore, it is more powerful than the "array". See the example below.

```
1     #include <iostream>
2     #include <vector>
3
4     int main()
5     {
6         std::vector<std::string> numbers;
7
8         numbers.push_back("one");
9         numbers.push_back("two");
10        numbers.push_back("three");
11
12        for (auto number: numbers)
13        {
14            std::cout << number << std::endl;
15        }
16
17        return 0;
18    }
```

In line 6, we declare a vector to be a container of strings, and we name it "numbers". In lines 8-10, we push into the back of the vector the strings listed. Note that it will have three elements. In line 12, we will iterate through the vector, declaring a variable "number" with the type "auto" (the type will be automatically set by the compiler). Inside the for-loop, the "number" will be loaded with each one of the elements of the "numbers" vector, and the program will print the "number" on the screen.

Please, search for "Containers" in C++. You will find several types, like "vector", "set", "map", "stack", "queue", and "deque". It is worth knowing that almost any type of container we may need, we will find it.

Functions 2

When we pass variables as arguments to functions, we do it "**by value**" or "**by reference**". When we pass by "reference", any changes in the variable will have an effect outside the function, at the original scope of the variable, whereas when by "value", the changes will have an effect only at the scope inside the function. Let us take an example.

```cpp
1    #include <iostream>
2
3    void myFunc(int i)
4    {
5        i = i + 1;
6        std::cout << "myVar at myFunc has the value: " << i << std::endl;
7    }
8
9
10   int main()
11   {
12       int myVar = 0;
13
14       std::cout << "myVar at main has the value: " << myVar << std::endl;
15       myFunc(myVar);
16       std::cout <<"myVar at main, after myFunc, has the value: " << myVar << std::endl;
17
18       return 0;
19   }
```

```
myVar at main has the value: 0
myVar at myFunc has the value: 1
myVar at main, after myFunc, has the value: 0
```

We can see in the example above that "myVar" was not changed after calling "myFunc". Now, let us call by "reference".

```cpp
1    #include <iostream>
2
3    void myFunc(int &i)
4    {
5        i = i + 1;
6        std::cout << "myVar at myFunc has the value: " << i << std::endl;
7    }
8
9
10   int main()
11   {
```

27

```
12        int myVar = 0;
13
14        std::cout << "myVar at main has the value: " << myVar << std::endl;
15        myFunc(myVar);
16        std::cout <<"myVar at main, after myFunc, has the value: " << myVar << std::endl;
17
18        return 0;
19    }
```

```
myVar at main has the value: 0
myVar at myFunc has the value: 1
myVar at main, after myFunc, has the value: 1
```

Observe that we have used the ampersand (&) before the parameter "i" at the definition of function "myFunc". This will inform C++ that we are passing the value by "reference". Any changes in the value will have an effect outside the function. Because of that, the value of "myVar" printed at main, after calling "myFunc", will be "1" instead of "0".

As a note, the parameters (int &i) and (int& i) or even (int & i) at the function declaration are equivalent. The ampersand can be at distinct positions with the same meaning.

Another way for the function to be able to change the value of the variable passed to it is to pass a "**pointer**" to the variable instead of the variable itself. Let us make another example.

```
1     #include <iostream>
2
3     void myFunc(int *i)
4     {
5         *i = *i + 1;
6         std::cout << "myVar at myFunc has value: " << *i << std::endl;
7     }
8
9
10    int main()
11    {
12        int myVar = 0;
13
14        std::cout << "myVar at main has value: " << myVar << std::endl;
15        myFunc(&myVar);
16        std::cout << "myVar at main, after myFunc, has value: " << myVar << std::endl;
17
18        return 0;
19    }
```

```
myVar at main has value: 0
myVar at myFunc has value: 1
myVar at main, after myFunc, has value: 1
```

Observe that we have passed the "&myVar" as an argument, and we have declared the parameter as "int *i" in the function definition, showing that we are dealing with a pointer. As a pointer stores the address of a variable, when we pass it and deference it (to access its value or change it), we are dealing with the original variable.

Another way of defining a function object is with the "**lambda**" expression. See the example:

```
1    #include <iostream>
2
3    int main()
4    {
5        int myVar = 0;
6
7        // create lambda
8        auto f1 = [&myVar]() { // myVar is passed by reference
9            myVar = myVar + 1;
10           std::cout << "myVar at f1 has the value: " << myVar << std::endl;
11       };
12
13       std::cout << "myVar at main has the value: " << myVar << std::endl;
14
15       // execute lambda
16       f1();
17
18       std::cout << "myVar at main, after f1, has the value: " << myVar << std::endl;
19
20       return 0;
21   }
```

```
myVar at main has the value: 0
myVar at f1 has the value: 1
myVar at main, after f1, has the value: 1
```

We can see that the function object is created in lines 8-11. There is not a separate function declaration, as viewed before, but all occur inside the main.

A lambda function has three parts: a "**capture list**" (that appears inside the [ ]), a "**parameter list**" (that appears inside the ( )) and the "**main part**" (that appears inside the { }).

Variables outside the main part of the lambda (outside the { }) cannot be accessed. If we need to access some external variable, we need to add it to the capture list. In the example, we have added the "myVar" by reference, so the "f1" can change the "myVar" value, and the modification will propagate to the main function.

The "parameter list" has the same meaning as when used in regular functions. See the example:

```
1    #include <iostream>
2
3    int main()
4    {
5        int myVar = 0;
6
7        // create lambda
8        auto f1 = [](int& i) { // "i" is declared by reference
9            i = i + 1;
10           std::cout << "myVar at f1 has the value: " << i << std::endl;
11       };
12
13       std::cout << "myVar at main has the value: " << myVar << std::endl;
14
15       // execute lambda
16       f1(myVar);
17
18       std::cout << "myVar at main, after f1, has the value: " << myVar << std::endl;
19
20       return 0;
21   }
```

```
myVar at main has the value: 0
myVar at f1 has the value: 1
myVar at main, after f1, has the value: 1
```

We see that the "f1" was able to change the value of "myVar" because we have declared the parameter "i" in the "parameter list" by "reference" (with an ampersand "&"). This is just what happens in regular functions.

Turning back to the "capture list", if we had passed "myVar" by value, there would have been a limitation, because in that case the lambda "f1" would not accept changing that value. We would have to put a "mutable" keyword before the "main part" to get it. See the example:

```
// create lambda
auto f1 = [myVar]() {  // myVar is passed by value
    myVar = myVar + 1; // error
    std::cout << "myVar at f1 has value: " << myVar << std::endl;
};
```

```
// create lambda
auto f1 = [myVar]() mutable { // myVar is passed by value
    myVar = myVar + 1; // ok
    std::cout << "myVar at f1 has value: " << myVar << std::endl;
};
```

Now, "f1" can alter the "myVar", but its modification will not propagate to the main because the variable was captured by value.

Classes 2

The classes are like a fabric of objects, having the "recipe" for them because each object we will define will have the same variable types, names, and methods (functions) of the class. The "**template**" concept in C++ can make the classes even more flexible by allowing classes with generic types. It is like a "recipe" of a "recipe".

With "generic types", we can define the types differently each time the object is instantiated. For example, if a class has a member variable of type "int", the same class can have the same member variable as "double". See the example below.

```
1    #include <iostream>
2
3    template <class SomeType>
4    class Point {
5    private:
6        SomeType _x;
7        SomeType _y;
8    public:
9        Point(SomeType x, SomeType y) { _x = x; _y = y; }
10       SomeType getX() { return _x; }
11       SomeType getY() { return _y; }
12       SomeType distance(Point other)
13       {
14           SomeType result;
15           result = sqrt(pow(_x - other.getX(), 2) + pow(_y - other.getY(), 2));
16           return result;
17       }
18   };
19
20   int main()
21   {
22       Point<int> p1 = { 0, 0 };
23       Point<int> p2 = { 3, 4 };
24       double d1 = p1.distance(p2);
25       std::cout << "Distance d1 is " << d1 << std::endl;
26
27       Point<double> p3 = { 0.001, 0.0 };
28       Point<double> p4 = { 3.0, 4.0 };
29       double d2 = p3.distance(p4);
30       std::cout << "Distance d2 is " << d2 << std::endl;
31
32       return 0;
33   }
```

Output:

```
Distance d1 is 5
Distance d2 is 4.9994
```

Comparing the lines 23-23 and 27-28 of the code above, we can see that we are using the class "Point" to create objects "p1" and "p2" that have integer points, and objects "p3" and "p4" that have double precision points. Therefore, the same class "Point" can work with different member variable types ("int" and "double"). This can be achieved by declaring a "**template**", as line 3 shows. After that, we also need to put the desired type between the angle brackets <> when creating the objects, like in line 22 (Point<int>) that informs the type "int".

Concurrency

Typically, when the computer is executing our program, or when we think in the algorithm, we are reasoning in a sequence of events. When we call a function, we need to wait for its execution before we start executing the next instruction. This is the "**synchronous**" path of execution.

However, we also can program the computer to execute the function while executing other things in parallel. In our example of the multi-ball collision simulator, we make the computer move the balls at the same time by functions that are running in parallel. This is called "**asynchronous**" execution: we do not have to wait. This is also called "**concurrency**" because we will have several codes wanting to run in the same CPU, concurring with its resources.

Some concepts to search are:

- "**parallel computing**", as a type of computation, and similarly "**concurrent computing**".
- "**synchronous**" and "**asynchronous**", referring to the path of execution.
- "**processes**" and "**threads**", relating to the resources (memory,
- "**address space**", processors, files, network connections) used by the program.
- "**concurrency**" support in C++, relating to the possibility of running multiple threads in parallel, and the "**pthread**" library.
- **<thread>** header in C++.
- "**std::thread**", the thread class.
- "**thread object**", relating to the creation of a thread.
- "**main thread**", relating to the thread where "main" runs.
- "**join**" and "**detach**", referring to the thread object.
- "**thread constructor**", relating to its nature of "**variadic template**", a "**template**" that takes a variable number of arguments.
- "**std::move**" and "**std::ref**", relating to the way we pass the arguments to the thread function.

In C++, we make this by assigning a function to run into a "**thread**". This will enable the function to share the same memory, accessing the same variables of the main program or other functions running on other threads in the same program, also called "**process**". Typically, a program will run in one process, while it can have one thread for running its main function and other threads for functions or other tasks, if we ask to, normally in an asynchronous path in this case.

For working with threads in C++, we need to use the "Thread" class that is given by the "thread" library. We create an object of type std::thread and pass to it the function we want to execute in parallel. After that, while the function is running, we need to call the thread member function "join", which will only return when the thread run has been completed. In this way, we can be waiting for the thread to finish. If we do not do that, our main function will finish, the program will terminate, and our thread will still be running! This is not correct and may cause issues with the system.

Let us do something interesting: start a thread without calling the "join". This is the code we are going to compile and run:

```
1    #include <iostream>
2    #include <thread>
3
4    void threadFunction()
5    {
6        int i = 0;
7        for (int i = 0; i < 3; i++) {
8            std::this_thread::sleep_for(std::chrono::milliseconds(100)); // simulate work
9            std::cout << "Work in a thread...\n";
10       }
11
12   }
13
14   int main()
15   {
16       // create thread
17       std::thread t(threadFunction);
18
19       // do something in main()
20       std::this_thread::sleep_for(std::chrono::milliseconds(50)); // simulate work
21       std::cout << "Finished work on main\n";
22
23       // wait for thread to finish
24       // t.join();
25
26       std::cout << "Finishing main\n";
27
28       return 0;
29
30   }
```

If we compile with g++, we need to include the support for the "pthread" library, with the flag "-pthread". For example, if the file above was named "Source.cpp", we need to command:

```
g++ Source.cpp -pthread
```

It is unnecessary if we compile using an IDE, like Microsoft Visual Studio[3].

In line 17, the program creates a thread and passes to it, as an argument, the function "threadFunction" that was declared in lines 4-12. The main code will print on the screen, even after the main thread has finished, causing an error (a debug error):

```
Finished work on main
Finishing main
```

---

[3] This book is neither affiliated with, nor authorized, sponsored, or approved by, Microsoft Corporation.

```
Work in a thread...
Work in a thread...
Work in a thread...
(Error message)
```

Now, if we call the "join" by uncommenting line 24, the main function will wait:

```
14    int main()
15    {
16        // create thread
17        std::thread t(threadFunction);
18
19        // do something in main()
20        std::this_thread::sleep_for(std::chrono::milliseconds(50)); // simulate work
21        std::cout << "Finished work on main\n";
22
23        // wait for thread to finish
24        t.join();
25
26        std::cout << "Finishing main\n";
27
28        return 0;
29
30    }
```

```
Finished work on main
Work in a thread...
Work in a thread...
Work in a thread...
Finishing main
```

We can see that the "Finishing main" was printed after the work was finished in the thread. The "main" function has waited for the "threadFunction" running on the "t" thread to conclude its job.

In line 17 of the code above, we have called the thread constructor, passing to it, as an argument, the "threadFunction", a function that we have created before. In fact, if we want, we can pass more arguments, which the constructor will interpret as the arguments to that function. Please, see the example:

```
1    #include <iostream>
2    #include <thread>
3
4    void threadFunction(std::string threadName)
5    {
6        int i = 0;
7        for (int i = 0; i < 3; i++) {
8            std::this_thread::sleep_for(std::chrono::milliseconds(100)); // simulate work
```

```
 9              std::cout << "Work in thread " << threadName << " ...\n";
10          }
11
12      }
13
14      int main()
15      {
16          // create thread
17          std::thread t(threadFunction, "Example");
18
19          // do something in main()
20          std::this_thread::sleep_for(std::chrono::milliseconds(50)); // simulate work
21          std::cout << "Finished work on main\n";
22
23          // wait for thread to finish
24          t.join();
25
26          std::cout << "Finishing main\n";
27
28          return 0;
29      }
```

```
Finished work on main
Work in thread Example ...
Work in thread Example ...
Work in thread Example ...
Finishing main
```

In line 4, the function was declared as having a parameter of type string. This will be printed in line 9. When we called the thread constructor, at line 17, we passed to it the name of the function and one string as arguments. Therefore, the thread constructor can receive a function and its arguments and will create a thread with those elements. This is possible because the constructor is defined with a "template", a "variadic" one, which can receive multiple arguments.

It is also possible to start threads with member functions. First, we create an object. Then, we call the tread constructor, passing to it the member function (the function that belongs to the class in which we have created the object), the object, and the arguments to be used by that member function. See the example at Ball.cpp, line 132 (no extra arguments are passed).

Now, our primary goal is to pass the data between threads.

This is a complex topic. You do not need to search for everything on the first try. After that, please see the examples below and become more familiar with the subjects. We will not use all these concepts in the code example at the end of the book, but it is worth mentioning them. Some concepts to search are:

- "**concurrency bugs**", relating to the errors we need to avoid in concurrent programming.
- "**data races**", relating to simultaneous reads and writes on shared data.
- "**critical sections**", the sections of the code to be protected from data races.
- **<mutex>** header in C++.
- "**std::mutex**", means "mutual exclusion", the class used to signal critical sections of code that need exclusive access.
- "**lock**" and "**unlock**", relating to the "**mutex**".
- "**std::lock_guard**" class, relating to the "**mutex**".
- **<future>** header in C++.
- "**std::promise**" and "**std::future**" class, for one-way communication between threads.
- "**future::get**", relating to the blocking of the thread until receiving the value.
- **<condition_variable>** header in C++.
- "**std::condition_variable**" class, relating to the blocking of the thread until notified.

When we program our code to run in parallel, for example, in the simulation where we make each ball play in a separate thread (so the balls are all running in parallel), we will need some communication between the threads. It is done by "shared variables". For example, each ball needs to know the position of the others. The shared variable will be the coordinates of the ball, but this kind of communication can result in errors. For example, if we are reading an "x" coordinate of a ball with position (x, y) while it has changed its position and just write a new (x, y) in its coordinates. We have just read the "x", but before we read the "y", this data has changed. The result will be that we will have read the old "x" and the new "y". It is wrong!

The code that contains the shared variables we must protect from simultaneous reads and writes is called the "critical section". When we have the read while the write is happening, it will be a "data race" problem. We can protect this section of the code by declaring an object of type "**mutex**" and calling the method "**lock**" at the beginning and "**unlock**" at the end of the section, so the other threads will not have access to it until the thread that is running finishes its job. The other threads will be waiting for the "unlock" of the section. Therefore, this kind of use brings some synchronization to an asynchronous path.

There is a simpler way. We do not need to manage the "**mutex**" if we use the "**lock_guard**". This use prevents the problem that can happen if an exception (an error) occurs while executing code in the critical section. If this happens, because the variables are "locked", the code will probably freeze. Because the "lock_guard" will automatically unlock when we are out of scope, when the object is destructed, or when the exception occurs, the freeze will not happen.

See the example in Appendix A, in the file CylinderObject.cpp, lines 30-32. We are using the "lock_guard" at several places in the code. This means that we are protecting the shared variables from data races, as the same code is going to be executed in several threads at the same time (one thread for each object that is running).

```cpp
void  CylinderObject::getPosition(double& x, double& y)
{
    std::lock_guard<std::mutex> lock(_mutex);
    x = _posX;
    y = _posY;
}
```

In the example above, we are reading the object position by calling the member function "getPosition", but only the thread that is running can access it so that it will access the "_posX" and "_posY" (which are the position of the cylinder) without interferences. These variables were protected from being changed while this thread was reading them. The other threads will wait.

Observe that the "x" and "y" are passed by reference, so when we make "x = _posX", the "x" will load the value of "_posX," and this will reflect outside the member function, altering what the "x" and "y" at the caller are.

Nevertheless, there are situations where threads need to communicate specific data to other threads, which will be waiting for the data. This is where the "**promise**" and "**future**" classes are useful. In this case, we do not have a shared variable but a specific channel of communication for one-time use. Please, search for the concepts.

In our code example in Appendix A, we are using another code structure, a "**message queue**" class, with the help of a "**condition_variable**" class and its member functions "**wait**" and "**notify_one**". It will work like a mailbox.

See the code:

```cpp
1   template <typename T>
2   class MessageQueue
3   {
4   public:
5       T receive();
6       void send(T&& msg);
7       int getSize();
8
9   private:
10      std::mutex _mutex;
11      std::condition_variable _cond;
12      std::deque<T> _queue;
13  };
14
15
16
```

```
17   template <typename T>
18   T MessageQueue<T>::receive()
19   {
20
21       std::unique_lock<std::mutex> uLock(_mutex);
22       _cond.wait(uLock, [this] { return !_queue.empty(); });
23
24       T msg = std::move(_queue.back());
25       _queue.pop_back();
26
27       return msg;
28   }
29
30   template <typename T>
31   void MessageQueue<T>::send(T&& msg)
32   {
33       std::lock_guard<std::mutex> uLock(_mutex);
34       _queue.push_back(std::move(msg));
35       _cond.notify_one();
36   }
37
38   template <typename T>
39   int MessageQueue<T>::getSize()
40   {
41       std::lock_guard<std::mutex> uLock(_mutex);
42       return _queue.size();
43   }
```

In lines 1-13, we have the class declaration. This piece of code could be separated and saved in a header file (a file with extension .h). It is possible to observe what are the variables and what the class will do by the name of the functions.

We can see that the class uses a "**template**" mechanism that makes part of the class, the variables that will store the messages, independent of the data type. Therefore, it is possible to construct a queue for each data type with this same class.

In line 12, we have the queue declaration. In lines 10-11, we have the "**mutex**" and the "**condition_variable**" objects declaration, which will be used to manage the protection of the critical section, which in this case has the queue variable itself.

In lines 5-7, we have the functions prototypes. There are three functions: "receive", "send", and "getSize". The first is used to receive messages from the queue, the second to send, and the third to get the queue size. The functions definitions are in lines 17-43.

At the beginning of each function, in lines 21, 33, and 41, there is a class ("**unique_lock**" or "**lock_guard**") that will manage the "**mutex**". This shows that we will have a critical section following.

In line 22, we are using a "condition variable" object, named "_cond", calling its function "wait", which will make the thread wait until it receives a signal (see line 35) and the queue is not empty. The "wait' has two arguments. The first is the "uLock", the object that is managing the "mutex". The second is a lambda function, which will return true only if the queue is not empty (that will happen when we have data on it or after we have written data in the queue).

We could think that as we are in the critical section, the queue is locked to be written, so it will be impossible for another thread to update it. However, the condition variable has the solution for this problem because it will temporally unlock the critical section until it receives a signal (from its function "notify_one"; see line 35) and will only unblock the thread (continues to execute the code after line 22) when the second argument of wait is true, or in this case, when the queue is not empty (when the queue is not empty, the lambda will return true).

Therefore, with the "send" function, lines 30-36, we write in the queue and send a signal to the condition variable in line 35. If we have a thread stopped in line 22, it will receive the signal, test if the queue is not empty, and as is the case, it will lock the critical section following, read the message from the queue (lines 24-25) and return the message (line 27).

When we need to have a class with a message queue to be able to send and receive messages from other threads, we just attach a message queue by declaring a member variable as a message queue object. For example, see line 88 at "Ball.h" in Appendix A. We have declared a "MessageQueue<CollisionData> _msgQueue" for communications between the "Ball" objects and the main function.

In line 87, in the main function, "Main.cpp" at Appendix A, we are starting a thread named "t1", passing to it as an argument a function "processPiston", and as one of the arguments to this function, the "balls" vector. In lines 451-616, we have defined the "processPiston" function.

Inside that function, in line 524, we will get the message received by the ball after verifying if there is some message (at line 521). We are calling the "receiveMsg" member function of the "ball". Seeing the "Ball" class, line 113 of the file "Ball.cpp", we can see that the function is calling the "receive" method from the "_msgQueue" object. This is the "receive" method of our "message queue", as illustrated above, or at lines 14-30 of "Ball.cpp".

We are sending the messages in the "play" function of the "Ball" class in lines 244-245. This function will be running at another thread, as we can see in function "simulate", at line 132 of "Ball.cpp". This function "simulate" is called at the main function, line 83. So, it will start another thread, and this thread will send the messages to the thread that is running the "processPiston" function, which is called at line 87 of the main function.

Practice 4

Let us do an exercise with a situation that will occur in our Multi-ball Collision Simulator, with two threads reading and writing on each other. The goal is to see if when one class locks its variables, the other cannot access it. Another is to see if when one class locks the variables of the other class, the other must wait until the unlock.

The code will have two objects that, each play, will change itself and the other. See below:

```
1   #include <string>
2   #include <mutex>
3   #include <vector>
4   #include <iostream>
5
6   std::mutex mtxCout;
7
8   class Board: public std::enable_shared_from_this<Board>
9   {
10  public:
11      Board() {
12          _message = "";
13          _id = _idCnt;
14          _idCnt++;
15          _waitTime = 0;
16      };
17      void setMessage(std::string message) {
18          _message = message;
19          printBoard();
20      }
21      void setWaitTime(int waitTime) { _waitTime = waitTime; }
22      void setBoards(std::vector<std::shared_ptr<Board>> boards) {
23          _boards = boards;
24      }
25      int getId() { return _id; }
26
27      void play() {
28          mtxCout.lock();
29          std::cout << "board(" << _id << ") begin of play() with " <<
30              "thread id=" << std::this_thread::get_id() << std::endl;
31          mtxCout.unlock();
32
33          // begin of critical section
34          board_mutex.lock();
35          // write on this board
36          setMessage("board(" + std::to_string(_id) + ") mutex locked");
37          std::this_thread::sleep_for(
38              std::chrono::milliseconds(_waitTime));
39
```

41

```cpp
40            for (auto board : _boards) {
41                // write on another board
42                if (board->getId() != getId()) {
43                    board->setMessage("board(" + std::to_string(_id) +
44                        ") writing on the board(" +
45                        std::to_string(board->getId()) + ")");
46                    std::this_thread::sleep_for(std::chrono::milliseconds(_waitTime));
47                }
48            }
49
50            setMessage("board(" + std::to_string(_id) + ") unlocked");
51            // end of critical section
52            board_mutex.unlock();
53
54            mtxCout.lock();
55            std::cout << "board(" << getId() << ") end of play()" << std::endl;
56            mtxCout.unlock();
57        }
58
59        void printBoard() {
60            mtxCout.lock();
61            std::cout << _message << std::endl;
62            mtxCout.unlock();
63        }
64
65        std::mutex board_mutex;
66
67    private:
68        static int _idCnt;
69        int _id, _waitTime;
70        std::string _message;
71        std::vector<std::shared_ptr<Board>> _boards;
72    };
73
74    int Board::_idCnt = 0;
75
76    int main() {
77        std::vector<std::shared_ptr<Board>> boards;
78        for (int nb = 0; nb < 2; nb++) {
79            boards.push_back(std::make_shared<Board>());
80        }
81        boards.at(0)->setBoards(boards);
82        boards.at(0)->setWaitTime(3000);
83        boards.at(1)->setBoards(boards);
84        boards.at(1)->setWaitTime(1000);
85        std::thread t0(&Board::play, boards.at(0));
86        std::thread t1(&Board::play, boards.at(1));
87        t0.join();
88        t1.join();
89    }
```

The core of the class is the function "play", lines 27-57. This function will print when it has started, showing the thread "id". After that, it will try to change the data of the other "board" (that is running on another thread). It will do that with the function "setMessage".

The "board" 1 has a shorter cycle (line 84), 1000ms compared to 3000ms of "board" 0. The purpose is to see if it can change the data inside "board" 0, when the "mutex" in that class (in "board" 0) be locked. Let us see the printed results:

```
board(0) begin of play() with thread id=15840
board(1) begin of play() with thread id=9028
board(0) mutex locked
board(1) mutex locked
board(1) writing on the board(0)
board(1) unlocked
board(1) end of play()
board(0) writing on the board(1)
board(0) unlocked
board(0) end of play()
```

As seen above, the "board" 1 succeed in changing the data inside "board" 0. This is because when the "board" 1 is writing in the "_message" of board 0, through the "setMessage", it is not locking the same "mutex" (the "mutex" of "board" 0), but only its own "mutex".

Therefore, the solution is to make a "lock" on the "mutex" of the other class, before calling the "setMessage". See the code:

```
for (auto board : _boards) {
    // write on another board
    if (board->getId() != getId()) {
        board->board_mutex.lock();
        board->setMessage("board(" + std::to_string(_id) +
            ") writing on the board(" +
            std::to_string(board->getId()) + ")");
        std::this_thread::sleep_for(std::chrono::milliseconds(_waitTime));
        board->board_mutex.unlock();
    }
}
```

We just created two statements inside the for-loop. One at the beginning, the other at the end, with the lock/unlock commands. However, the result was:

```
board(1) begin of play() with thread id=13496
board(1) mutex locked
board(0) begin of play() with thread id=13984
board(0) mutex locked
```

The code will halt here and show an error message. The reason is that as one thread is already locked, it is not possible to lock it again. When the "board" 1 tries to lock the mutex of "board" 0, it has already been locked by the "board" 0, so it is not possible to lock it again. It must be unlocked. However, the "board" 0 will only unlock after the for-loop and succeed in locking the "board" 1. Therefore, both threads will be waiting for the other to complete, but it will not be possible because it depends on a lock of something already locked. This is a scenario called a "deadlock".

Instead of having a mutex for each object, we can make the mutex "static", so all the objects will share the same (it will belong to the class):

```
static std::mutex board_mutex;
```

The other adjustment is the necessity of declaring the static variable in the global context, just before the "main" function:

```
int Board::_idCnt = 0;
std::mutex Board::board_mutex;

int main() {
```

Now the results will be:

```
board(0) begin of play() with thread id=936
board(1) begin of play() with thread id=7372
board(0) mutex locked
board(0) writing on the board(1)
board(0) unlocked
board(0) end of play()
board(1) mutex locked
board(1) writing on the board(0)
board(1) unlocked
board(1) end of play()
```

The goal was achieved. We can see that the "board(0)" starts locking the mutex. After that, it will complete its work without the interference of "board(1)". Nevertheless, if we have multiple boards, with each one locking the same mutex, we will have lost the benefits of parallelism since the threads will be running like a synchronous path.

The SDL Library

As we have stated, we think that the three major pillars of successful programming are the knowledge of the language (syntax and semantics), the IDE and its resources, and finally, what will leverage our work, the knowledge of the libraries.

In the code example at the end of this book, we will use the "**SDL Library**", or **Simple DirectMedia Layer Library** [3]. We have made a brief summary of how to use it.

Installation

The first procedure to install a library is to go to the developer site and search for instructions. Normally, you will find it separated by operational systems. Try to search for the "Wiki" pages. Usually, you will also find tutorials.

For Debian-based Linux, like Ubuntu, you just need:

```
$sudo apt-get install libsdl2-dev
```

For Windows, you can make an integrated install with Microsoft Visual Studio[4], so it would be possible to access the SDL header directly from the editor.

First, install the **vcpkg** package manager, which can be found at:

```
https://github.com/Microsoft/vcpkg
```

Download the .zip or clone the repository. Choose a place for the `vcpkg-master` directory. Open a Command prompt terminal (with just user rights). Change to it and run the installation file (you do not need the administrative account):

```
> cd vcpkg-master
> bootstrap-vcpkg.bat
```

Then, command the integration with Microsoft Visual Studio:

```
> vcpkg integrate install
```

---

[4] This book is an independent publication and is neither affiliated with, nor authorized, sponsored, or approved by, Microsoft Corporation.

Then, install `sdl2`:

```
> vcpkg install sdl2:x86-windows
```

To use the header file `SDL.h`, use the autocomplete from Microsoft Visual Studio when typing the header. Eventually, you will need to reinstall when you upgrade the IDE.

Rendering an image

Below is a summary of the major commands for rendering an image.

```
1   // Initialization of SDL, window and renderer
2   SDL_Window* gWindow = NULL;
3   SDL_Rebderer* gRenderer = NULL;
4
5   SDL_Init( SDL_INIT_VIDEO );  // initialize SDL; > 0 success
6   SDL_SetHint( SDL_HINT_RENDER_SCALE_QUALITY, "1" );// set texture filtering to linear; true
7
8   gWindow = SDL_CreateWindow( "Title", SDL_WINDOWPOS_UNDEFINED, SDL_WINDOWPOS_UNDEFINED,
9   SCREEN_WIDTH, SCREEN_HEIGHT, SDL_WINDOW_SHOWN ); // SDL_... are the SDL constants
10
11  gRenderer = SDL_CreateRenderer( gWindow, -1, SDL_RENDERER_ACCELERATED |
12  SDL_RENDERER_PRESENTVSYNC );
13
14  SDL_SetRenderDrawColor( gRenderer, 0xFF, 0xFF, 0xFF, 0xFF );
15
16  int imgFlags = IMG_INIT_PNG;
17  ( IMG_Init( imgFlags ) & imgFlags );  // initialize PNG loading; true;
18
19  // Loading the texture from file
20  SDL_Texture* mTexture;
21  int mWidth;
22  int mHeight;
23  SDL_Texture* newtexture = NULL;
24
25  SDL_Surface* loadedSurface = IMG_Load ( path.c_str() );
26  SDL_SetColorKey( loadedSurface, SDL_TRUE, SDL_MapRGB( loadedSurface->format,0,0xFF,0xFF));
27  newTexture = SDL_CreateTextureFromSurface( gRenderer, loadedSurface );
28
29  mWIdth = loadedSurface->w;
30  mHeight = loadedSurface->h;
31  SDL_FreeSurface( loadedSurface );
32
33  mTexture = newTexture;
34
35  // Setting texture color, blend, and alpha
36  SDL_SetTextureColorMod( mTexture, red, green, blue); /*declare and define the arguments*/
```

```
37    SDL_SetTextureBlendMode( mTexture, blending );
38    SDL_SetTextureAlphaMod( mTexture, alpha );
39
40    // Clearing screen
41    SDL_SetRenderDrawColor( gRenderer, 0xFF, 0xFF, 0xFF, 0xFF );
42    SDL_RenderClear( gRenderer );
43
44    // Rendering
45    SDL_Rect* clip;
46    double angle;
47    SDL_Point* center;
48    SDL_RenderFlip flip;
49    SDL_Rect renderQuad = { x, y, mWidth, mHeight };
50    if( clip != NULL ) {
51        renderQuad.w = clip->w;
52        renderQuad.h = clip->h;
53    }
54    SDL_RenderCopyEx( gRenderer, mTexture, clip, &renderQuad, angle, center, flip );
55
56    // Updating screen
57    SDL_RenderPresent( gRenderer );
58
59    // Unloading the texture
60    SDL_DestroyTexture( mtexture );
61    mTexture = NULL;
62    mWidth = 0;
63    mHeight = 0;
64
65    // Closing the SDL
66    SDL_DestroyRenderer( gRenderer );
67    SDL_DestroyWindow( gWindow );
68    gWindow = NULL;
69    gRenderer = NULL;
70    IMG_Quit();
71    SDL_Quit();
```

Rendering a text

Now, we have the commands for rendering a text.

```
1     // Initialization of SDL, window, and renderer
2     .../* the same statements as above for initialization */
3
4     // Loading the font form file
5     TTF_Font *gFont = NULL;
6     int fontSize;
7     gFont = TTF_OpenFont( path.c_str(), fontSize );   // TTF_GetError()
8     SDLColor textColor = { 0, 0, 0 };
9
10    // Loading a text in the texture
11    SDL_Texture* mTexture;
12    int mWidth;
```

47

```
13    int mHeight;
14
15    SDL_Surface* textSurface = TTF_RenderText_Solid( gFont, textureText.c_str(), textColor );
16    mTexture = SDL_CreateTextureFromSurface( gRenderer, textSurface );
17
18    mWidth = textSurface->w;
19    mHeight = textSurface->h;
20    SDL_FreeSurface( textSurface );
21
22    // Rendering
23    .../* the same statements as above for rendering */
24
25    // Closing the font
26    TTF_CloseFont( gFont );
27    gFont = NULL;
28
29    // Quit SDL subsystem
30    TTF_Quit();
```

Legal Notice

Below there is a transcription of the legal notice about the **Simple DirectMedia Layer** library license from the site **libsdl.org** [4]:

```
"SDL 2.0 and newer are available under the zlib license :

This software is provided 'as-is', without any express or implied
warranty.  In no event will the authors be held liable for any damages
arising from the use of this software.

Permission is granted to anyone to use this software for any purpose,
including commercial applications, and to alter it and redistribute it
freely, subject to the following restrictions:

1. The origin of this software must not be misrepresented; you must not
   claim that you wrote the original software. If you use this software
   in a product, an acknowledgment in the product documentation would be
   appreciated but is not required.
2. Altered source versions must be plainly marked as such, and must not be
   misrepresented as being the original software.
3. This notice may not be removed or altered from any source distribution."
```

The Multi-ball Collision Simulator

Program structure

Here we will explain the program structure, using the program in Appendix A, by studying its main blocks.

The title of this subchapter is about explaining the software. However, it is more appropriate to use the word "conquering". This is because knowledge is like a property, and we are speaking about this not only to explain but to understand, to be able to change, and to use it in another idea. This is a paradigm change: not be the user, but be able to program, to create.

The first step is asking a question: Why? Is this use of time and energy worth it?

We think that first, we must analyze the results of the program itself. One of our favorite simulations is with several balls initially at rest, without gravity, and the piston with gravity, like this:

```
GAS_MODE 0
NBALLS 8
BALL_RADIUS 8
BALL_SPEED 0
BALL_MASS 0.2
BALL_GRAVITY 0
IS_TESTING 0
BALL0_SPEED 10
BALL0_VEL_ANGLE 0
BALL1_SPEED 10
BALL1_VEL_ANGLE -180
PISTON_MASS 10
PISTON_GRAVITY 10
BOTTOM_TEMP_MIN 0
BOTTOM_TEMP_MAX 100
```

The simulation will result in a beautiful sequence of collisions, and at some time, they will change. At that point, we can think there is a transition from order to disorder. We can grasp the real meaning of random processes.

Observing and simulating real phenomena reaches not only our knowledge or our reasoning but our feeling, something above the simple reason. It is like giving an upgrade in the reasoning, with consequences far beyond what was initially planned.

So, the answer is yes! Nevertheless, there is more.

The program is not extensive. It has a relatively simple structure, so one person alone can understand it and be able to change it to implement other ideas. It uses one of the fastest execution languages, C++, which can produce very optimized binaries so that the computers can execute it amazingly fast. We think that for this kind of simulation, this language is powerful!

Therefore, the definitive answer is a double yes!

So, from where do we start? From the "main" function, which is at "Main.cpp" in Appendix A?

That is the standard because the "main" is the starting point. However, it is worth seeing the general file structure, observing the names, and trying to link to the program results.

With the concepts seen above, we will try to understand the program in Appendix A.

The first step is to see the general structure of it by observing the names of the files, seeing that some names have the .h and corresponding .cpp, and there is a file with the name "Main.cpp", suggesting that this is the starting point of the program.

We can see that the files Constants.h and Globals.h have only "constants" and "variables" declarations. In the CylinderObject.h, Ball.h, and Wall.h, we have class definitions and its functions declarations, and in the corresponding .cpp files (CylinderObject.cpp, Ball.cpp, Wall.cpp), we find its functions definitions.

We also have the file "Parameters.txt". As the name suggests, it has the parameters that will be loaded by the program for selecting the characteristics of the simulation.

The last two files, with "cmake" inside their names, will have configuration parameters for the building process.

Now that we have a general idea, we can observe that the program has comments everywhere. This will help, but it is worth an explanation of the program structure.

The big picture

The software was planned based first on a general view. This is a view of the main blocks, what they will do and what will be the corresponding classes. The big picture contains two classes, the Ball and the Cylinder, and the starting point, the control center of the program, which is the Main function, as shown below:

Ball

- A ball will have the ability to update its position based on its velocity.
- When it collides with another ball or object, it will be able to change its own position.
- It can be on a gravity field so that it will update its position based on its mass.

Cylinder

- The cylinder will contain all the balls. It will be formed by the letterals, the piston, and the base.
- The letterals are fixed as the base. The piston will move based on its mass and gravity and the collision of the balls.

50

Main

- The main function will create the objects, the cylinder, and the balls.
- It will be responsible for loading the parameters and putting each object to work.
- It will render the canvas and control the program.

Comparing the description above with that of Appendix A, we can see an important difference. The Cylinder class does not exist! This is because the description is only a general idea. The implementation is a little different: the cylinder is formed by the Wall class. We will have two walls, left and right, and the top (the piston, which will move) and the bottom (that will simulate some heat).

The Ball and the Wall will inherit from the CylinderObject class because all the objects have some aspects in common. For example, they have a location (x, y) on the space (on the canvas). They will get velocity, speed, and mass. See the file "CylinderObject.h", which has the declaration or prototype of the class, and the file "CylinderObject.cpp", which has the definition or implementation.

Starting from the data analysis, we can observe the major data that the class will manage. See the file "CylinderObject.h", lines 44-46. See the corresponding getters and setters (the functions that will load the values or read them) in lines 25-34.

When we analyze the "Wall.h", we see that this class inherits from "CylinderObject" (see line 4 and the declaration in line 13). This class will have more data, as shown by lines 36-38. The wall will have height and can have a temperature (as in the case of the bottom). Observe that the wall can have "type", and the types are defined by an "enum class" at line 6. The implementation of the class is in the file "Wall.cpp".

The "Ball" will also inherit from "CylinderObject" but will add more data, as shown by lines 82-86 of the file "Ball.h". The implementation is in file "Ball.cpp". It is important to note that together with the "Ball", we have the class "MessageQueue", at lines 15-27 of file "Ball.h", also implemented in "Ball.cpp".

We see at line 88 of "Ball.h" that the "Ball" will have an object of type "MessageQueue" as a member variable. This will be used to pass messages from the balls to the Main function, specifically to the function that is processing the piston movement. See the line 524, inside block 519-538, of "Main.cpp". There it will be receiving collision data by calling the function "receiveMsg", which is implemented at lines 111-114 of "Ball.cpp". We can see that this function will call the "receive" function of the message queue object attached to the ball as a member variable.

The Main.cpp

In this file, as seen in Appendix A, we have 854 lines where there is the "main" function and other functions that will be called by the "main". The "main" function (lines 54-200) is the starting point of the program, which is where the program begins to execute. The auxiliary functions are first declared before the "main", in lines 25-51, and then implemented after it in lines 203-854.

At the beginning of the file, lines 1-10 are the commands to use (to "include" in the current file) some standard libraries, and in line 11, we have the command for the SDL library. In lines 13-16, we specify the inclusion of the files where we have declared the classes and some variables, the constants, and that with global scope.

Below is a simplified schematic of the "main" function.

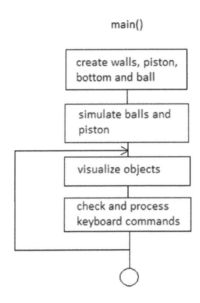

Figure 2 - Diagram of the main function.

In lines 58-75, we create the objects according to the type of simulation chosen. In lines 77-87, we simulate the balls and the piston. They will be running on separate threads. In lines 89-185, we visualize the objects (the balls and the cylinder, with its parts, the piston, the bottom, and the lateral walls). In lines 187-199, we process the finishing of the program by closing the renderer and asking the threads to stop.

We have a loop in lines 100-183, where we will be rendering the objects (printing them on the screen) and monitoring the keyboard for commands, which can be for changing the injection of energy by the bottom of the cylinder (an approximation of a temperature change), or for closing the window. The last one will be interpreted as a command for stopping the program and exiting.

In lines 203-304, we implement the function "createObjects", which will create all the objects for the simulation. Observe that its arguments were passed by reference so that any change will propagate to the main. There, at the main, we first declare the vectors and pointers in lines 59-62, and after we pass them to "createObjects" in line 69.

In "createObjects", in lines 207-241, we will create the four walls of the cylinder and then assign the bottom and the piston pointers to their walls in lines 236 and 240.

Before creating the balls, we need to know where to put them initially. So, in lines 243-276, we will divide the interior of the cylinder, considering just a two-dimension plane, into cells, like a grid, and load this data in the "places" vector (line 261; line 275).

In lines 279-296, we will create the balls, as many as the value of the global variable "nballs", and set their positions according to the "places" coordinates (line 282). We will set the ball speed, mass, gravity, and type of simulation at lines 292-295. Observe that at line 292, the ball is assigned a random velocity direction. In lines 299-303, each ball will know about the other balls and walls of the piston, so they will be able to find themselves and process collisions.

In lines 306-353, we will have the function "initRenderer". It will call the SDL library methods necessary for the renderer and will define the global variables used in the renderer process. These global, the "gWindow" and the "gRenderer", are "smart pointers" that will be pointing to the window and renderer objects created with the proper calling of the SDL functions. In lines 355-358, we just have the "closeRenderer", which will call the proper SDL function for closing the renderer (freeing the memory).

In lines 360-449, we will have the functions "renderBall", "renderWalls", and the helper function "drawCircle" that will be used by the "renderBall". Observe that the functions will get as arguments the pointers to the ball and to the walls vector, to know the positions (line 402; line 420) and sizes (line 403; line 421), and will use the "gRenderer" global variable to make the drawings.

In lines 451-616, we will have one of the most important functions, the "processPiston", which will compute the piston position according to the simulation state. It will be running on a specific thread, as shown in line 87. We will explain it in a separate subchapter.

In lines 719-854, we have the function that presents the initial menu to the user. It will print on the screen some pre-defined options for the simulation, including one that will load the parameters from a file, so the users can write any values they want.

See, for example, the variable definitions in lines 746-755. This is for option "1" (case "1" in the switch statement). It will define the "gas_mode" (the type of the simulation: 0 for normal and 1 for "gas"); "nballs" (the number of balls in simulation); "ball_radius" (the ball radius); "ball_speed" (the ball speed: absolute value or velocity modulus); "ball_mass" (the ball mass); "ball_gravity" (the ball gravity: it is possible to choose a different gravity for the balls as a set); "piston_mass" (the mass of the piston); "piston_gravity" (it is possible to choose a gravity only for the piston).

In the option "5", the program will first verify if there is a file (or if there is a file in the proper directory, which is the same directory where the program is running). It will do that by calling the function "loadParametersFromFile". If there is no such file, it will load some default values.

The "loadParametersFromFile" is defined at lines 619-693. It is worth comparing the lines 671-689 with the file "Parameters.txt" in Appendix A. You will see the correspondence between the upper-case parameters name and the lower-case global variables. It is also worth comparing with the file "Globals.h".

In the simulation, we need to adjust some variables in order to change the simulation parameters, so we will be able to simulate several conditions. These variables were defined with global scope and can be loaded from a file. They appear in lines 671-689 of the "loadParametersFromFile" (file "Main.cpp") and at the file "Parameters.txt".

Comparing the file "Globals.h", which has the global scope variables, with the file "Parameters.txt", both in Appendix A, there is a correspondence between each global variable with an upper-case parameter with the same name. This means that every global variable that is used for the simulation parameters can have its value changed by loading it from the file.

In the simulation menu, function "chooseSimulation", lines 719-854 of file "Main.cpp", we can define (change the value of) several of the global variables, except those from lines 11-15 of "Globals.h". Those variables will control the "testing" mode, which is a mode where there will be two balls with specific velocities (modulus and direction). The default is "is_testing = 0" as defined in "Globals.h", so that mode will not work. If we want to choose the velocities from the two first balls, we need to set the "is_testing" to "1". See lines 71-75 of "Main.cpp". Immediately after creating the objects (and the balls), we will redefine the first two balls if "is_testing" is greater than zero.

The "testing" mode is useful for specific collisions and can be configured in the "Parameters.txt", choosing "NBALLS 2", setting the "IS_TESTING 1", and the balls' speeds and angles.

Therefore, the "Main.cpp" has the "main" function and some other functions called by the "main". It will control the simulation, load the data, and render the simulation on screen. Now we will explain the function "processPiston".

The "processPiston" function

The "processPiston" function, at lines 451-616 of the file "Main.cpp" will set the piston position (the y axis position) based on the number of collisions received during a time interval and the energy of the balls relevant to the collision (their velocities at y-axis direction). The model assumes perfect elastic collisions and no friction. It will be applying the Linear Momentum-Impulse Theorem and The Law of Conservation of Linear Momentum, roughly simulating a gas, if we choose a great number of balls with small mass and high speed (and no gravity, to improve the result). Please, see more in the references [5] and [6].

The function also has the role of tracking some variables and printing them to the screen, as can be viewed in lines 491-502. For that, we have declared a lambda function "f0" at line 471-506, which will run on a separate thread "t1", called at line 508.

The lambda will run a loop (line 474) while the variable "finish" is false. This is the signal sent to the lambda when the function must terminate. Inside that loop, it will count the number of balls in the interior of the cylinder (lines 478-489) and will print this value with others (lines 491-502). We see that only in the "gas" mode (line 494) we will print the up-force average that the balls are doing and the downforce (by the gravity) on the piston. Below is a simplified schematic of the "processPiston" function.

processPiston()

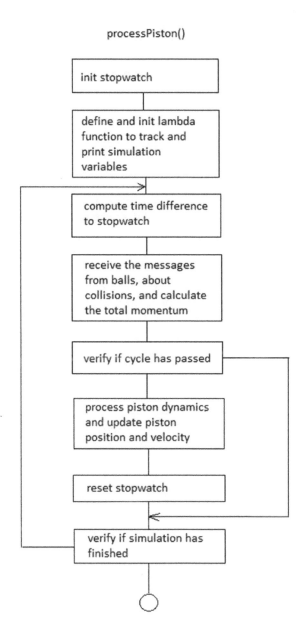

Figure 3 - Diagram of "processPiston" function.

In lines 519-538, we will receive the messages from balls about collisions, and we will calculate the total linear momentum, which will be saved in the "mv" variable (line 534). In line 524, we call the "receiveMsg" ball member function, which will return a value of type "CollisionData". This type is defined in lines 35-38 of the file "Ball.h", which is included in "Main.cpp" (line 15). The data has the type of collision (if with the "bottom" or the "piston") and the "y" axis velocity, so we can calculate the linear momentum (line 534).

In lines 542-606, we have a code that, if a cycle has passed, will process piston dynamics (applying the physics equations) and will update its position and velocity. In this case, it will reset the total momentum variable "mv" in line 600, update the temperature variable "temp" of the bottom (line 601), and will reset the stopwatch for the next cycle in line 604.

Now it is time to study the "Ball" class.

The "Ball" class

We start by seeing the class prototype that is in file "Ball.h" in Appendix A.

The "Ball" class prototype is at lines 40-92 of the file "Ball.h". In line 40, we can see that the class inherits from the "CylinderObject" class and from the "enable_shared_from_this" class. The latter is necessary for the objects of the class to be able to create instances of "shared_ptr" pointing to themselves.

Because of the inheritance, we need to view the "CylinderObject.h" file, which is where the "CylinderObject" class is declared (the prototype). We must analyze both the "CylinderObject" class together with the "Ball" class declaration in the "Ball.h".

In the "public" members of the "CylinderObject" class, at lines 18-38, we can see the getters and setters of position, velocity (in the "x" and "y" directions), speed, and mass. So, all these functions will be used by the objects of the "Ball" class. Their respective variables are in the "protected" members, lines 44-46.

In line 48, we can see part of the "thread barrier", the vector that will hold the threads that will be launched for running some member function of the object. The other part is at the destructor definition, as can be seen in the file "CylinderObject.cpp", lines 67-73. There, we have a "for_each" loop, which will run a lambda function whose role will be to call a "join" in each thread stored in the vector "_threads". This will guarantee that the threads will finish when the object is destructed or before the program finishes.

After the "_threads" vector, we will have in lines 50-51 two "mutex", one for protecting the member attributes (or the critical section where these variables will be accessed) and the other to protect the standard "cout" (the text screen output). The latter will be "static" because all "CylinderObject" objects will share it.

In the "private" members, we have the identity number of the object, which is also static because it will be shared.

Except when the definition of the member functions is only one statement, for example, the "getID" (line 23) and the "getType" (line 35), all the implementation of the functions is in a separate file, in the "CylinderObject.cpp". There, we can see the constructor in lines 8-19, the getters and setters in lines 21-65, and the destructor in lines 67-73. Therefore, the "CylinderObject" class is the first approach to the objects that we are using. One more specialized class is the "Ball" itself.

The core of the "Ball" class is the function "play" (lines 136-402 in the file "Ball.cpp") that is called by "simulate" (lines 127-133 in the file "Ball.cpp"). The "simulate" starts a new thread to run the "play", saving the thread in the "_threads" vector for the "thread barrier" strategy.

The "play" will give movement to the ball and will detect and process the collisions. So, when a ball collides with other, it is in this function that the physics equations will be applied to calculate the new velocities.

Ball:play()

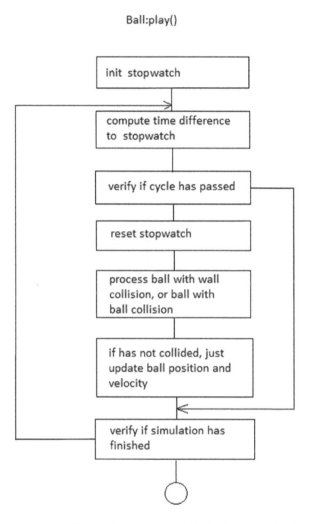

Figure 4 – Diagram of "Ball::play" member function.

In lines 186-328 of file Ball.cpp, the Ball::play will process ball with wall collisions. If the collision is with laterals or with the bottom, it is simpler because they are fixed, so we just need to change the velocity of the ball, the normal component relating to the wall. We can see this processing in lines 259-325.

In lines 192-257, there is the ball with piston collision. In this case, there are two alternative types of processing: we consider that the piston is another object colliding with the ball, or we count the number of balls colliding during a time interval and send this information to the piston, by the message queue (lines 244-245), for the function that is processing the piston dynamics, the "processPiston" (file "Main.cpp", as can be seen at lines 521-537). That function is running on a separate thread and will process this information, applying the Linear Momentum-Impulse Theorem (file "Main.cpp", lines 545).

In lines 334-384, we have the ball with ball collision. In the function "resolveCollision", which is called in lines 366-369, we will apply the physics equations to calculate the new velocities of the ball and its counterpart. The "resolveCollision" is implemented at lines 477-584 and will apply The Law of Conservation of Linear Momentum and the Conservation of Energy (because the model considers perfect elastic collisions). Thus, it will only change the components of velocity along the line of collision and consider the deformation impulse equal to the restitution impulse. Please, see more in the references [7] and [8]. It will also push balls apart after the collision to eliminate the intersecting.

One of the best things about the models and the computer programs is the ability to alter the software and see what happens, learning with the process. There is a two-way road: the program will try to explain how the physical world works, and by observing this and paying attention to any difference, we must explain to the program what the physics equations are.

Consequently, the program teaches us, and we correct the program. This is a remarkably interesting learning process. In our case, we have a challenge and a learning opportunity. For example, knowing that the system is closed, with no energy escape, do you think that is the simulation below correct?

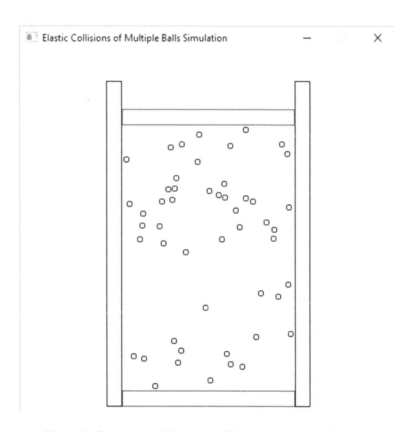

Figure 5 - Simulation of 50 balls colliding, gas mode, initial stage.

This is the simulation with 50 (fifty) balls, in the "gas" mode, option 4 (four) of the menu, in the initial stage, the first seconds of simulation time. The piston has gravity and mass and is falling, compressing the balls that have no gravity and small mass.

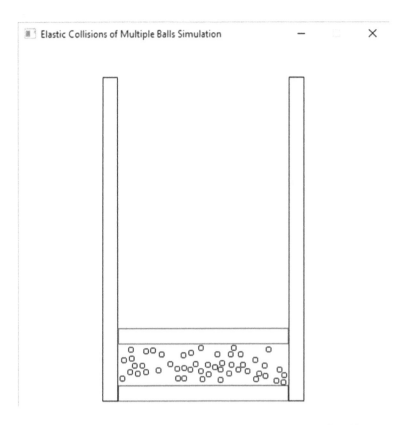

Figure 6 - Simulation of 50 balls colliding, gas mode. After 200
seconds, the piston almost stopped at the lower position.

After some time, the balls will stay all near the bottom, with small velocities. This is not correct and appears like an energy escape. Therefore, the simulation model, represented by the diagram and its implementation in the "Ball::play" function, presents a small error, which appears as a small decrease in the energy of the system. The challenge is to discover what is happening. The reward is the learning improvement. Hint: What is energy in this case?

Energy Escape

There is a small loss of energy observed in the simulation. We can see in figure 4 that if the ball has not collided, the algorithm instructs just to update the ball position and velocity. This means that the concern with the effect of gravity was left to be considered only after the collisions. The ball is entering the collision with its original velocity and only after the effect of gravity is computed. See line 173 of file "Ball.cpp", in the function "play", where the program calculates the increase in velocity, "y" axis component, caused by gravity ("dVy"). This increase will only be added in case of ball-ball collision, after the event, at line 372. When there is no collision, it is added at line 391, as shown by the diagram in figure 4. Finally, nothing is added when colliding with the piston, bottom, or walls. Therefore, the work of gravitational force seems not to be done in this case, during the cycle or the time interval when collisions happen.

Try to do the following experiment and see the results. First, comment (usually with "//" at the beginning of the line) the statement that updates the velocity if there is no collision (line 391). Also, comment on the statement that updates ball velocity after the ball-ball collision, when "setVelocity" is called with "velY + dVy" as an argument (line 372). Instead of this statement, put another just updating with "velY" (and "velX").

Then, go to before the collisions processing, and create a statement to update the velocity "velY", adding "dVy" to it, and call "setVelocity" for updating the velocity in the ball, like this:

```
velY += dVy;
setVelocity(velX, velY);
```

This must happen before the ball with wall collision (before that "for loop" of line 187). Consequently, we will give the ball more velocity before entering the collisions.

Energy Excess

There is another possible error. If we use the "gas mode", where the piston will be moved by counting the total linear momentum change of the balls during the cycle, we will have a considerable error if we make the ball mass equivalent to the piston mass. This is because the "gas mode" considers that the balls, like gas particles, must have a small mass compared to the wall and will collide and reverse the movement, preserving the module of the velocity component that is parallel to the line of collision and inverting its direction. In the "gas" model, the piston, with much greater mass, will not move or be affected by only one ball. As in the "gas", many more collisions would be needed for the piston to be affected.

We can verify the error in the "gas" mode, in the case of greater ball mass, by doing the simulation:

```
GAS_MODE  1
NBALLS  1
BALL_RADIUS  20
BALL_SPEED  0
BALL_MASS  10.0
BALL_GRAVITY  0
IS_TESTING  0
BALL0_SPEED  30
BALL0_VEL_ANGLE  0
BALL1_SPEED  0
BALL1_VEL_ANGLE  -180
PISTON_MASS  10.0
PISTON_GRAVITY  1.0
BOTTOM_TEMP_MIN  0.0
BOTTOM_TEMP_MAX  100.0
```

It is possible to see that the piston is obtaining energy. What is wrong! Compare it with the standard model, where:

```
GAS_MODE  0
```

We can adapt the "gas" mode to process this kind of collision, with balls with greater mass, by passing as a message to the "processPiston", not the relative velocity of collision, but the change in velocity of the ball. In the "processPiston", we get this and calculate the change in momentum. So, the modifications could be:

In "Ball.cpp", line 208, we save only the ball velocity "y" component before collision:

```
double velCollisionGas = velY;
```

In "Ball.cpp", line 244-245, we send the total change in "y" velocity, as "velY" is the velocity after the collision:

```
_msgQueue.send({ CollisionType::pistonCollision,
                 velCollisionGas - velY });
```

In "Main.cpp", line 534, we compute the change in momentum:

```
mv += ball_mass * velocity;    // change in momentum
```

Observe that the line numbers are based on the original program, the same as Appendix A. After this improvement, the comparison of the models will show that the two models will have closer responses.

Our goal with this book and the software has been achieved at this stage. Nevertheless, as we stated, this software is an invitation to new applications. We will try to incorporate two things, the Elastic Collisions and Newton's Law of Gravitation, into each ball (and try to roughly simulate the universe!).

The first improvement demands the application of the coefficient of restitution "e", which will be zero when the collision is "**inelastic**" and one when "**elastic**" (the actual case). This coefficient represents the relation between the deformation impulse and the restoration impulse. Please, see more in the references [7] and [8]. It is also the relation between the relative velocity of receding after impact and the relative velocity of approach before impact:

```
(v2f - v1f) = e * (v1i - v2i)
v1: velocity of ball 1
v1i: v1 initial
v1f: v1 final
e: "coefficient of restitution"
```

First question: Where do we need to apply this "coefficient of restitution"?

The answer is where the ball movement is processed. For that, we need to understand the application of the physics equations at the software level.

We know that at "Ball.cpp", in the "Ball::play", we have sections of code that process the ball with wall and ball with ball collisions. We have a helper function "resolveCollision" that will apply the equations to the collision of two balls. Let us start by it.

The "resolveCollision" is at lines 477-584. At line 489, we have the "angleCol", which will represent the angle of the line of collision. Only velocities parallel to this line will be changed by the collision. The perpendicular components will remain the same (because there will be no impulse acting on them).

In lines 490 and 491, we have the direction of the velocities of the first ball and second ball (other), represented by the angles: "direction" and "otherDirection". In lines 493-494, we calculate the parallel component (speed * cos) and the perpendicular component (speed * sin) to the line of collision for the first ball. In lines 496-497, we do the same for the second. We will name the line of collision as "xspeed" and the perpendicular as "yspeed", so we will have "new_xspeed" and "new_yspeed" for the components of the first ball; "new_xspeedOther", "new_yspeedOther", for the components of the second.

At this point, the problem will be just computing the collision along the line of collision based on the parallel components. See lines 503-504. The final "yspeed" components will be the same, so now the problem will get one dimension, the final "xspeed", which is along the line of collision. This is done in lines 499-500, where we apply both equations, the Conservation of Linear Momentum and the coefficient of restitution equal to one, representing the Conservation of Kinetic Energy.

The lines 506-515 will reconstruct the velocity components relative to the "x" and "y" axes. For example, line 510 will reconstruct the "x" component by adding the projections relative to the "x" axis of the parallel (+1*cos) and perpendicular (-1*sin) velocities components.

Therefore, the coefficient needs to be applied in lines 499-502. However, before that, we need to create a global variable, "**coef_rest**", in the file "Globals.h" in the ball values. We also need an argument in "resolveCollision", "**coef_e**", store it in the "Ball" class as a member variable "_coef_e", and define it when creating the ball, in the "createObjects", with value "coef_rest". Finally, we must modify the "loadParametersFromFile" (in "Main.cpp") to be able to read the data from the "Parameters.txt" (COEF_RESTITUTION 1.0) and the "printParameters".

Thus, we have the "coef_e" and need to apply it to lines 522-525. We have made the substitutions, and the result is:

```
double final_xspeed = ((mass - coef_e * otherM) * new_xspeed +
    (otherM + coef_e * otherM) * new_xspeedOther) / (mass + otherM);
double final_xspeedOther = ((mass + coef_e * mass) * new_xspeed +
    (otherM - coef_e * mass) * new_xspeedOther) / (mass + otherM);
```

It is possible to see that if "coef_e" were zero, the two velocities would be equal, and the final linear momentum would be the sum of each initial linear momentum. Please, make the simulation to confirm:

```
GAS_MODE  0
NBALLS  2
BALL_RADIUS  20
BALL_SPEED  0
BALL_MASS  10.0
BALL_GRAVITY  0
COEF_RESTITUTION 0.5
IS_TESTING  1
BALL0_SPEED  50
BALL0_VEL_ANGLE  0
BALL1_SPEED  0
BALL1_VEL_ANGLE  -180
PISTON_MASS  10.0
PISTON_GRAVITY  0.0
BOTTOM_TEMP_MIN  0.0
BOTTOM_TEMP_MAX  100.0
```

In this case, it is possible to see that the final relative velocity will be half of the approach.

Having made the adjustment to the ball-ball collisions, we must change the ball-wall collisions. Starting with the ball-piston collision, we just set the argument "coef_e" of "resolveCollision" to equal the "ball" restitution coefficient. We can define this, for example, after entering the "for loop":

```
// process ball with wall collision
for (auto wall : _walls) {

    // process piston->ball elastic collision (the piston moves in y axis):
    // m0*v0i + m1*v1i = m0*v0f + m1*v1f
    // Ec0i + Ec1i >= Ec0f + Ec1f

    // we will have between elastic and inelastic collisions
    double coef_e = getCoefRestitution();

    if (wall->getWallType() == WallType::piston)
    {
```

The following simulation tests the case. We set the ball to collide with the piston, which will have much greater mass. Verify that for each collision, the ball decrease velocity by the "coef_e".

```
GAS_MODE   0
NBALLS   1
BALL_RADIUS   20
BALL_SPEED   0
BALL_MASS   0.1
BALL_GRAVITY   0
COEF_RESTITUTION 0.5
IS_TESTING   1
BALL0_SPEED   50
BALL0_VEL_ANGLE   90
BALL1_SPEED   0
BALL1_VEL_ANGLE   -180
PISTON_MASS   100.0
PISTON_GRAVITY   0.0
BOTTOM_TEMP_MIN   0.0
BOTTOM_TEMP_MAX   100.0
```

In the case of ball-wall lateral and bottom, we just approximate by considering that the final velocity of the wall is zero. So, we just multiply by "coef_e". The following simulation tests the case. Verify that in each lateral collision, the ball decrease velocity by the "coef_e".

```
GAS_MODE   0
NBALLS   1
BALL_RADIUS   20
BALL_SPEED   0
BALL_MASS   10.0
BALL_GRAVITY   0
COEF_RESTITUTION 0.5
IS_TESTING   1
BALL0_SPEED   50
BALL0_VEL_ANGLE   0
BALL1_SPEED   0
BALL1_VEL_ANGLE   -180
PISTON_MASS   10.0
PISTON_GRAVITY   0.0
BOTTOM_TEMP_MIN   0.0
BOTTOM_TEMP_MAX   100.0
```

In the case of a collision with the piston, we did not change the algorithm for the "gas" mode, but we sent the message (to "processPiston" in "Main.cpp") about the velocity, subtracted by the "return" velocity calculated with "resolveCollision". So, we deliver less change in momentum.

Now we will apply Newton's Law of Gravitation, making each ball a source of a gravitational field. We will compute the total field in each ball and calculate the force to change the ball's velocity (as if it were gravity, but in that direction).

When we implemented this and the inelastic collision capabilities, we experienced several errors. Because of that, we have unveiled a new version of the software, which is in Appendix B.

The Newton's Law of Gravitation was processed by this part of the code (in the new version), in the "Ball.cpp" file, Ball::play member function:

```
202        // calc gravitational/force field
203        // F = G * m1 * m2 / r^2
204        // Gf = G * m2 / r^2
205        int thisBallId = getID();
206
207        double Gf = 0.0;      // field
208        double Gfx = 0.0;
209        double Gfy = 0.0;
210        double coef_G = getG();
211        double dGVx = 0.0;
212        double dGVy = 0.0;
213
214        if (coef_G > 0 || coef_G < 0)
215        {
216            for (auto ball : _balls)
217            {
218                int otherBallId = ball->getID();
219                if (thisBallId != otherBallId)
220                {
221                    double otherX, otherY;
222                    ball->getPosition(otherX, otherY);
223
224                    double m2 = ball->getMass();
225                    double r = distanceToPoint(posX + dx/2, posY + dy/2,
226                        otherX, otherY);
227                    Gf = coef_G * m2 / (r * r);
228                    double angle = atan2(otherY -posY -dy/2, otherX -posX -dx/2);
229                    Gfx += Gf * cos(angle);
230                    Gfy += Gf * sin(angle);
231                }
232            }
233
234            // calc gravitational acceleration effect
235            dx += 0.5 * Gfx * pow(timeSinceLastUpdate / 1000.0, 2.0);
236            dy += 0.5 * Gfy * pow(timeSinceLastUpdate / 1000.0, 2.0);
237
238            dGVx = Gfx * (timeSinceLastUpdate / 1000.0);  // dV = A*dt
239            dGVy = Gfy * (timeSinceLastUpdate / 1000.0);
240        }
```

```
241
242                    // update velocity before entering the collision
243                    velX += dGVx;
244                    velY += dVy + dGVy;
```

From lines 221 to 227, we calculate the gravitational field produced by each one of the other balls, and in lines 228-230, its components are in the "x" and "y" axes. Therefore, in lines 229-230, we just sum those components to obtain the actual field at the place of the current ball.

In lines 235-236, we apply the acceleration to calculate the position displacement for the current ball during this cycle. That is added to the displacement already calculated, which has applied the velocity only. Now, the displacement takes the acceleration effect. Likewise, in lines 238-239, we get the velocity increase caused by the acceleration.

Finally, in lines 243-244, we just update the velocity. Observe that the "y" component velY is added by the dVy (velocity increase due to _ball_gravity) and dGVy (velocity increase due to gravitational acceleration).

Are there software limits?

It is worth observing that even in nature if we push the variables to the extreme, unplanned things can happen. For example, if we push a ball into a wall, at some velocity, the wall or the ball would break. At this point, we think that the software errors could also be viewed as a hint for those real things. This is again an iterative[5] learning process! It does not mean that there could be no errors in the software, but that the errors need to be interpreted to see if they are algorithm errors or have more fundamental or physical reasons.

The software in Appendix B, in comparison with the software in Appendix A, illustrates the possibilities of the entire process and the power of computing for creative expression, which will have only a limit on our imagination.

---

[5] It may be an "interactive" learning process also, because we are reacting to the software outputs that are showing the errors or inconsistencies of our model.

Below are instructions for Linux and macOS systems and Windows.

Linux and Mac

Dependencies are other software, like libraries, build tools, or compilers, needed to build and run the program on your computer (locally).

Below, there is a list of such dependencies with their minimum versions and the instructions about their installation.

- `cmake >= 3.5`
  - All OSes: installation instructions at the developer site <https://cmake.org/install/>.

- `make >= 4.1 (Linux, Mac)`
  - Linux: "make" is installed by default on most Linux distros.
  - Mac: install Xcode Command Line Tools to get "make" <https://developer.apple.com/xcode/features/>.

- `SDL2 >= 2.0`
  - All installation instructions can be found at <https://wiki.libsdl.org/Installation>, as well as in the chapter "The SDL Library".
  - Note that for Linux, an `apt` or `apt-get` installation is preferred to build from the source.

- `gcc/g++ >= 5.4`
  - Linux: gcc / g++ is installed by default on most Linux distros.
  - Mac: same deal as "make" - install Xcode Command Line Tools <https://developer.apple.com/xcode/features/>.

You must create a directory that will be the "root" project directory. Choose any name, for example, "MbcsProjectCmake". Then, you need to create two sub-directories, the "src" and the "build".

After that, you need to copy the files from Appendix A, except the "sdl2-config.cmake" (or copy the files from Appendix B, plus the "CMaleLists.txt" from Appendix A) into the proper directories that you have just created.

The final folder structure will be like this:

```
<ROOT PROJECT FOLDER>
    <src>
        Ball.cpp
        Ball.h
        Constants.h
        CylinderObject.cpp
        CylinderObject.h
        Globals.h
        Main.cpp
        Parameters.txt
        Wall.cpp
        Wall.h
    <build>
        Parameters.txt
    CmakeLists.txt
    README.md
```

With the files ready, you need to "build" the program. Open a terminal and type these basic "build" instructions:

1. Starting at the "root" project directory, change to the "build" directory:

   ```
   $ cd build
   ```

2. Generate the make files (the .. means we are pointing to the directory above, which is where there is the "CmakeLists.txt" with instructions to the "cmake"):

   ```
   $ cmake ..
   ```

3. Compile:

   ```
   $ make
   ```

4. Run the program!

   ```
   $ ./MbcsProjectCmake
   ```

Inside the "build" will appear more files, the compiler-generated output files. For a clean installation, just delete them.

In Linux, if you edit some files, or change some content, just repeat the process starting from the "make" command. It will automatically detect which file was changed and will rebuild the program with it.

On Windows, we have used the Microsoft Visual Studio[6], which is an IDE and can be found here <https://visualstudio.microsoft.com/>. This tool uses the Visual C++ compiler suite (MSVC compiler) and its own build process. It can also use the "Cmake" and can target a Linux machine for compilation over the network, but this is an advanced topic and will be addressed later.

After installing the Microsoft Visual Studio, we need to install the package for working with the C++ language. Please, go to the menu "Tools" > "Get Tools and Features..." to open the installer and select "Desktop development with C++" for the installation. After that, install the SDL2 library also, as shown in the chapter "The SDL Library".

When we have installed all the prerequisites, we will be ready to create a "project" or a "solution" (this is the name, actually). Open the Microsoft Visual Studio, and you will see a new window with the menu "Get started" on the right. Choose "Create a new project", and select "Empty Project". Observe that there is a "C++" in the description. Give it a name, for example, "MbcsProject".

A new window will open, with a menu "File", "Edit", "View", and other options at the top. Then, on the right, we will have the "Solution Explorer" window. This will show the directory structure, but we have two modes. The standard will show the "Project" view. The other is the "Folder" view. The views can be switched by clicking on an icon at the icon bar of the Solution Explorer window. In the "Project" view, we will see the folders "Header Files", "Resource Files", and "Source Files".

We need to right-click on the "Header Files" and choose to "Add" a "New Item...". Then, we select "Code" (at left) and "Header File (.h)" (at right) for creating a header file. We must change the default name "Header.h" with "Constants.h", for example, to start creating the program that is in Appendix A. Click on the created file using the "Solution Explorer" window. It will open the "Text Editor" window. Now, we just need to write the code that is in Appendix A, file "Constants.h", on the editor window. Please, delete the "#pragma once" because it will not be necessary. Hint: after writing the code, use the "Edit", "Advanced", "Format Document", or "Format Selection", from the Microsoft Visual Studio, for the right indentation of the code.

Please, repeat the process for all the header (.h) files. Then, for the other files, the process is almost the same but in different folders. The "Parameters.txt" will be inside the "Resource Files" (select "Utility", "Text File", on the "Add New Item" window). The source code files (.cpp) will be inside the "Source Files" (select "Code", "C++ File"). We do not need to put the "CmakeLists.txt" or the "sdl2-config.cmake" inside the project folders. These are for Linux or Cmake projects, not for the MSVC building system.

When all the files are in place, all we have to do is to command "Build" and "Build Solution" from the menu. The "build" will show an error at this time, probably because we need to finish the SDL2 configuration. We must manually configure the Linker. We must go to the menu "Project",

---

[6] This book is an independent publication and is neither affiliated with, nor authorized, sponsored, or approved by Microsoft Corporation.

"Properties…", "Linker", click on the ▶ to open the Linker submenu, choose "Input", "Additional Dependencies" box, click on <Edit…>, and add "SDL2main**d**.lib" file in case of "**D**ebug" configuration (the standard), or "SDL2main.lib" file, for the "release" configuration.

Finally, we command "Debug" and "Start Debugging" for running the code in the "debug" mode (the IDE will be monitoring the execution in this mode).

Installation on Windows and Microsoft Visual Studio to create a Cmake project (advanced topic):

In Microsoft Visual Studio, we need first to install the "C/C++ Linux Development" workload. Go to the "Tools" menu, "Get Tools and Features…", and install the workload. After that, create a folder and create all project files. Create all that are in Appendix A or all from Appendix B (plus the "sdl2-config.cmake" from Appendix A).

Open the folder with the Visual Studio (using the option "Open a local folder"). The Microsoft Visual Studio will see the 'CmakeLists.txt' and will try to configure itself but will show an error.

In the configuration, GUI of the 'Cmake' (menu "Project", "Cmake settings"), choose the "x86-Debug" configuration (panel at right) and see the SDL2_DIR variable at the "Cmake variables and cache" at the center. Point that to the directory where you extracted the SDL2 development package. For example, point to "…/SDL2-2.0.10", which has the version number of the SDL. Mark the box "Save to JSON" for saving the configuration. In that SDL2 folder, also create a file "sdl2-config.cmake", as shown in Appendix A. This ".cmake" file will instruct the Cmake in the building process. This will configure "Cmake" (after having gone there by the SDL2_DIR) to point to the SDL libraries.

Now the error was gone. But for running, it is necessary to have a copy of the "SDL2.dll" in the same folder as the ".exe" of the project. Copy the "SDL2.dll" that is located at the "<SDL2_DIR>\lib\x64" or "<SDL2_DIR>\lib\x86" to the folders that are inside the project folder, "out\build\x86-Debug" or "out\build\x64-Debug" respectively. These folders were generated by the Microsoft Visual Studio in the building process. Also, we must change the #include <SDL.h> of the "Main.cpp" to #include <SDL2/SDL.h>.

It is possible to target a remote machine running Linux for the building process. In this case, we need to create a new configuration, for example, "Linux-Debug", and use the "Connection manager" in the "Cmake Settings" menu ("Project", "Cmake Settings") to configure a connection. In this case, the program will be compiled in the remote machine. We also need to change the "Toolset", choosing "linux_x86," for example and have installed the "Cmake", "gcc", "gdb", and "rsync", and "zip" on the remote machine.

In a typical configuration, for a local building, in the "Cmake Settings", we just choose the "x86-Debug" configuration, which will use the "msvc_x86" toolset. In this case, we also need to point the "SDL2_DIR" (from the Cmake variables) to the directory of the "SDL" (usually "SDL2-<version>") and mark it to save it in the JSON file as shown above.

In case of building error, in most cases, it is possible to solve it by observing the error messages. Try to think carefully about the message. Search on the internet about the matter. Make the necessary effort to understand its meaning.

It is important to observe that when we are building the C++ project with the "MSVC compiler toolset", which is the standard that is included in Microsoft Visual Studio, we have to set the build configuration as "Debug" and "x86", for the `#include <SDL.h>` of `Main.cpp` to be able to locate the library because we have installed the "x86" library and not the "x64".

We are explaining the usage based on the program in Appendix A. The program in Appendix B has the same usage but with more menu options and configuration parameters, and that in Appendix C has even more.

The "Parameters.txt" file, which should be located in the same folder as the executable, will contain parameters that the user can adjust, like the number of balls, the initial ball speed, the piston, or the ball mass, and others.

There is a "menu" with some example simulations, but it is possible to load parameters from a file:

```
Please, choose one example or read parameters from a file:
[1] Three balls. (default)
[2] One ball at rest. Piston with gravity.
[3] Eight balls at rest. Piston with gravity.
[4] Fifty balls (gas simulation approximation). Piston with gravity.
[5] Load parameters from a file.

Option:
```

If the user chooses only two balls (with option 5) and sets the IS_TESTING to 1, the user can adjust the speed and angle of the velocity vector of the two balls to simulate a specific collision. If the IS_TESTING is 0, the velocities will be randomly configured.

After choosing the option, the program will print the parameters for the user to verify. This is an example:

```
Please, verify the simulation parameters:

GAS_MODE 0
NBALLS 3
BALL_RADIUS 20
BALL_SPEED 60
BALL_MASS 0.1
BALL_GRAVITY 0
IS_TESTING 0
BALL0_SPEED 10
BALL0_VEL_ANGLE 0
BALL1_SPEED 10
BALL1_VEL_ANGLE -180
PISTON_MASS 100
PISTON_GRAVITY 0
BOTTOM_TEMP_MIN 0
BOTTOM_TEMP_MAX 100

Press enter to continue...
```

73

In a physical simulation, the complexity is huge, and the software is slightly inexact because we can see an exceedingly small decrease in the energy of the system.

We can put energy, as approximation, increasing the cylinder bottom temperature with the left key. During simulation, extra data about the mean force applied by the balls is printed to the console:

```
Time:0  balls:80    gas avg(1.0s) up force : 37.76    piston down force: 100.00    ~temp(bottom) : 0.00
Time:1  balls:80    gas avg(1.0s) up force : 76.65    piston down force: 100.00    ~temp(bottom) : 0.00
Time:2  balls:80    gas avg(1.0s) up force : 85.07    piston down force: 100.00    ~temp(bottom) : 0.00
Time:3  balls:80    gas avg(1.0s) up force : 88.65    piston down force: 100.00    ~temp(bottom) : 0.00
Time:4  balls:80    gas avg(1.0s) up force : 76.72    piston down force: 100.00    ~temp(bottom) : 0.00
Time:5  balls:80    gas avg(1.0s) up force : 108.61   piston down force: 100.00    ~temp(bottom) : 0.00
Time:6  balls:80    gas avg(1.0s) up force : 149.78   piston down force: 100.00    ~temp(bottom) : 0.00
Time:7  balls:80    gas avg(1.0s) up force : 75.26    piston down force: 100.00    ~temp(bottom) : 0.00
Time:8  balls:80    gas avg(1.0s) up force : 134.64   piston down force: 100.00    ~temp(bottom) : 0.00
Time:9  balls:80    gas avg(1.0s) up force : 120.86   piston down force: 100.00    ~temp(bottom) : 0.00
Time:10 balls:80    gas avg(1.0s) up force : 70.12    piston down force: 100.00    ~temp(bottom) : 0.00
```

To stop the simulation, just close the graphics window and, after, the console window. See the messages about the closing of the threads.

The program in Appendix B has improvements over that of Appendix A, like the Inelastic Collisions and Gravitational Simulations with Newton's Law of Gravitation. Because of this, the "Parameters.txt" will have 36 (thirty-six) variables, as shown in Appendix B. The menu will show new options also. Please, see the respective chapters and Appendix B.

The program in Appendix C has even more improvement, with the simulation of a "virus" propagation, with a simplified model. Please, see the respective chapter and Appendix C.

Planet and Satellite

```
GAS_MODE   0
NBALLS   2
BALL_RADIUS   8
BALL_SPEED   0
BALL_MASS   1.0
BALL_GRAVITY   0
BALL_G 1
PUSH_PULL 1
COEF_RESTITUTION 1.0


IS_TESTING   1
BALL0_SPEED   100.0
BALL0_VEL_ANGLE   0
BALL0_X 600
BALL0_Y 100
BALL0_RADIUS 8
BALL0_MASS 1e-6
BALL0_TIME 0
BALL0_DELTA_SPEED 1e-6
BALL0_DELTA_ANGLE 0


BALL1_SPEED   0
BALL1_VEL_ANGLE   0
BALL1_X 600
BALL1_Y 600
BALL1_RADIUS 50
BALL1_MASS 50.0


PISTON_MASS   1e10
PISTON_GRAVITY   0.0
BOTTOM_TEMP_MIN   0.0
BOTTOM_TEMP_MAX   100.0


BACKGROUND 1
SCREEN_WIDTH 1200
PERCENT_WIDTH 0.90
SCREEN_HEIGHT 1200
PERCENT_HEIGHT 0.90
WALL_WIDTH 20
ZOOM_FACTOR 0.50
```

Table 1 - Planet and Satellite

We are going to make some simulations, with the version in Appendix B, setting the "Parameters.txt" file for each one. When you see the expression "[…]", this means that we are omitting some unnecessary data.

The first example will be the simulation of a planet (a massive ball) and its satellite. The planet radius is not important, but we are going to set it for illustration purposes.

The cylinder will be the microcosms, where exist only one planet and its satellite. This is an oversimplified model but will illustrate Newton's Law of Gravitation, as well as the difficulty of doing the correct calculations in a real-time simulation. See the new "Ball::play" function to observe that we had to make some adjustments before an acceptable result. In our case, the satellite was not stable. Its orbit was increasing. However, after the adjustments, the orbit becomes better.

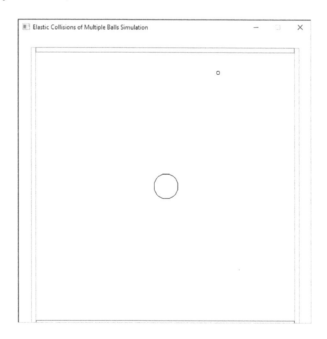

Figure 7 - Planet and Satellite.

We could see that after 10 min, the satellite still had the same orbit. The software apparently presented an acceptable result, confirming its purpose as a tool for studying physics and computer science. In fact, after 5000 seconds, or approximately 800 periods, the orbit was still stable!

Applying the equivalence between the gravitational force and the centripetal force (please, see more in the references [9]), we can verify if the software is applying the correct equations. We see that the orbit starts with a distance of 500, based on the difference between "BALL0_Y" and "BALL1_Y". The "BALL1_MASS" is 50.0, and the "BALL0_MASS" (the satellite) can be neglected (1e-6). The gravitational constant G in our fictional universe is 1 * G_mult (a global constant, in file "Globals.h"), which will result in 1e5, only for simplification. The equation is:

$$\frac{GMm}{r^2} = m\frac{v^2}{r}$$

With G = 100000, M = 50, cancelling both "m", and r = 500, do we have the result v = ?

Compare with "BALL0_SPEED"! Was the speed correct?

Launching a Satellite

In the previous example, we have launched the satellite already in its circular orbit path. Now, we are going to try launching from the planet's surface. This is a simplified model, and the software may have some imperfections. However, it will illustrate important concepts of physics and even the difficulties which are natural in the real-time simulations.

At this time, there will be a challenge for you. We are not going to give the exact procedure or values. You will have to think, use the physics equations and the software resources (just setting the appropriate values in "Parameters.txt"), and elaborate a strategy.

We are going to launch using two procedures. In the first one, we will try to launch just by setting the initial velocity and angle, launching from the surface. In the second, it will be possible to set another increase in velocity at a given time after the launching.

Observe that this is a real-time simulation, so the computer will use its internal clock to apply the equations, simulating the things like we have a parallel imaginary universe. If the computer is not fast enough, or the software has some imperfections, this will appear and produce errors.

The idea is to put the ball, representing a "satellite", in a "y" coordinate that will touch the border of the second ball, the "planet" at rest. Both will have the same "x" coordinate. Besides, in reality, the planets are in rotation. In fact, if we put the reference on the planet, it will be at rest relative to the ball (satellite).

Our fictional planet will have a radius of 200, and the satellite will have a radius of 12. Initially, the orbit was planned to be 400 (the distance between the centers), or equivalently, 200 from the planet's surface.

```
GAS_MODE  0
NBALLS  2
BALL_RADIUS  8
BALL_SPEED  0
BALL_MASS  1.0
BALL_GRAVITY  0
BALL_G  1
PUSH_PULL  1
COEF_RESTITUTION 1.0

IS_TESTING  1
BALL0_SPEED ...
BALL0_VEL_ANGLE  ...
BALL0_X 1000
BALL0_Y ...
BALL0_RADIUS 12
BALL0_MASS 1e-6

BALL0_TIME ...
BALL0_DELTA_SPEED ...
BALL0_DELTA_ANGLE ...

BALL1_SPEED  0
BALL1_VEL_ANGLE  0
BALL1_X 1000
BALL1_Y 1000
BALL1_RADIUS 200
BALL1_MASS 50.0

PISTON_MASS  1e10
PISTON_GRAVITY  0.0

BOTTOM_TEMP_MIN  0.0
BOTTOM_TEMP_MAX  100.0

BACKGROUND 1
SCREEN_WIDTH 2000
PERCENT_WIDTH 0.90
SCREEN_HEIGHT 2000
PERCENT_HEIGHT 0.90
WALL_WIDTH 20
ZOOM_FACTOR 0.40
```

Table 2 - Launching a Satellite

The "Parameters.txt" at the left illustrates the launching, but some values were omitted.

We need to know how much energy is necessary to leave the satellite in orbit, considering the potential energy differences between the two configurations: 1) at the surface and 2) orbiting. This energy will be given in the form of kinetic energy, so it determines the initial velocity of the launch.

We had made modifications to the program, as shown in Appendix "B", to give the spaceship (the ball) an impulse to increase its velocity after some time when we turned on a power source. If we adjust the appropriate values, we can give the satellite a velocity in the direction tangential to the orbit, with a value enough to compensate for the centripetal force and stabilize the orbit. This is what we have seen in the previous example.

The file "Parameters.txt" will have three more variables, the "BALL0_TIME" (the time in milliseconds when the auxiliary power turns on), the "BALL0_DELTA_SPEED", which is the speed added to the satellite, and the "BALL0_DELTA_ANGLE", which is the direction of the speed. In case, we will choose the direction to result in a velocity tangential to the circular orbit.

If we are using the two-stage launching, we need to know when to turn on the second power source.

We have made other modifications to the program, so it will print when the speed is near zero. Launching a satellite (ball 0) with an angle perpendicular to the surface (90 degrees) will give us a hint for that because we need only to observe when the velocity becomes near zero and annotate the time (which is in milliseconds).

We have made a launching, and even after 90min or more than 180 periods completed, the orbit has remained stable!

```
Time:3922        balls:2   ~temp(bottom) : 0
speed: 108.769   >>> orbit:423.003 <<<

Time:3923        balls:2   ~temp(bottom) : 0
speed: 108.788   >>> orbit:422.927 <<<

Time:3924        balls:2   ~temp(bottom) : 0
speed: 108.801   >>> orbit:422.877 <<<

Time:3925        balls:2   ~temp(bottom) : 0
speed: 108.806   >>> orbit:422.858 <<<

Time:3926        balls:2   ~temp(bottom) : 0
speed: 108.803   >>> orbit:422.87 <<<

[…]

Time:5637        balls:2   ~temp(bottom) : 0
speed: 108.66  >>> orbit:423.428 <<<

Time:5638        balls:2   ~temp(bottom) : 0
speed: 108.693   >>> orbit:423.299 <<<

Time:5639        balls:2   ~temp(bottom) : 0
speed: 108.724   >>> orbit:423.177 <<<

Time:5640        balls:2   ~temp(bottom) : 0
speed: 108.753   >>> orbit:423.065 <<<

Time:5641        balls:2   ~temp(bottom) : 0
speed: 108.777   >>> orbit:422.973 <<<
```

Table 3 - Orbit speed and distance

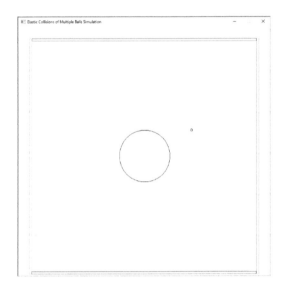

Figure 8 - Launching a Satellite.

For the launching, we need to set IS_TESTING 1 and set BALL0_SPEED with some value, and set BALL0_VEL_ANGLE with the initial direction of the velocity.

If we need a new impulse after some time, we must also set BALL0_TIME with the time in milliseconds and the BALL0_DELTA_SPEED with the increase in the current speed.

When BALL0_TIME is set to zero (BALL0_TIME 0), the statements that increase the velocity will be ignored by the program (see file "Ball.cpp", lines 246-255, p. 135). Otherwise, in a two-stage launching (when both BALL0_TIME and BALL0_DELTA_SPEED are different from zero), the program will print the speed and orbit distance (in relation to the center of the planet) after entering the second stage (see file "Piston.cpp", lines 82-91, p. 148; and "Ball.cpp", line 254). When only BALL0_DELTA_SPEED is different from zero, the program also prints the orbit (like in "Table 1").

In a two-stage launching, when the current speed in the first phase is below 1.0 or the ball is near the zero kinetic energy, the program will print the speed, time, and orbit (see "Ball.cpp", lines 260-272, and "Ball.cpp", line 254). Thus, in a perpendicular launching (90 degrees), having enough BALL0_TIME (greater than the time needed for the velocity inversion), it is possible to watch the time taken to reach the maximum altitude.

Launching a satellite is a remarkable experience, even in a simplified simulation.

```
GAS_MODE  0
NBALLS  63
BALL_RADIUS  8
BALL_SPEED  0
BALL_MASS  3.0
BALL_GRAVITY  0
BALL_G 1
PUSH_PULL 0
COEF_RESTITUTION 0.85

IS_TESTING  0
[…]




PISTON_MASS  1e10
PISTON_GRAVITY  0.0

BOTTOM_TEMP_MIN  0.0
BOTTOM_TEMP_MAX  100.0

BACKGROUND 0
SCREEN_WIDTH 4200
PERCENT_WIDTH 0.90
SCREEN_HEIGHT 2800
PERCENT_HEIGHT 0.90
WALL_WIDTH 100
ZOOM_FACTOR 0.3
```

We are going to build our fictional universe, where Newton's Law of Gravitation will work. This universe will have the size of 4200 * 0.90 on the "x" axis and 2800 * 0.90 on the "y" axis. It will have 63 balls, as shown below.

In the first simulation, the ball radius will be 5.0 and the ball mass 3.0. We turned off the "push-pull" section (setting as PUSH_PULL 0) of the "resolveCollision" function at the "Ball.cpp" file.

We are using a "zoom factor" of 0.3, so we can see all the points' coordinates on the screen. Initially, the balls are spaced along with the space, without speed.

Figure 9 - Gravitational Simulation.

After a while, we have the formation of a cluster of balls, with some balls making an orbit like a movement around for some time. This is remarkably interesting!

In fact, besides this simulation, we have used a radius of 8 instead of 5 for the balls. With a radius equal to 8.0, some simulations will not produce the satellites. But with a smaller radius, the balls were not being shown on the printing because of the low resolution of the print screen. So, we have changed to a greater radius for printing purposes.

In our universe, it is possible to change the variables and evaluate the results. For example, if we change the universe size to 30000 * 0.90 vs. 20000 * 0.90 and the "zoom factor" to 0.04, we will see that the balls move (slowly because the gravity force is smaller) towards the center but fail to form the cluster, and after that, they move toward the borders.

While in the first case, we have a cluster in a few seconds, in the second, it seems to be much more difficult to appear, as if it were impossible. So, in principle, we have concluded that the matter density (the number of balls per unit area) makes the difference.

```
GAS_MODE  0
NBALLS  3
BALL_RADIUS  8
BALL_SPEED  0
BALL_MASS  1.0
BALL_GRAVITY  0
BALL_G  1
PUSH_PULL  0
COEF_RESTITUTION  0

IS_TESTING  0
[…]




PISTON_MASS  1e10
PISTON_GRAVITY  0.0

BOTTOM_TEMP_MIN  0.0
BOTTOM_TEMP_MAX  100.0

BACKGROUND  0
SCREEN_WIDTH  300
PERCENT_WIDTH  0.90
SCREEN_HEIGHT  200
PERCENT_HEIGHT  0.90
WALL_WIDTH  10
ZOOM_FACTOR  2.0
```

Another interesting simulation is with just two balls, and after, with three balls for comparison. We have used the last one (with NBALLS 2 and NBALLS 3) and reduced the universe size, to 3000 * 0.90 vs. 2000 * 0.90, with the "zoom factor" 0.40.

We can see that the two balls form a cluster after a few seconds. However, when we introduce a disturbance in its initial alignment, introducing a third ball not perfectly aligned (just use NBALLS 3), after several minutes, the cluster has not still formed.

It is worth saying that the simulation results must also be thought of in terms of the software imperfections.

For example, if we make a simulation of 3 balls, with ball radius 8.0 and ball mass 0.1, coefficient of restitution zero, on a board size of 300 * 0.90 vs. 200 * 0.90, zoom factor 2.0, wall width 10, we will have a cluster of three balls, almost at rest, as we would expect. But, if we change the ball mass to 1.0 (as at left), we can see that the balls will rotate.

This is probably because of the small misalignment between the centers, which will produce a torque, and a rotation. As a result, when the gravitational force is not enough to the necessary centripetal force, the object "escapes" the gravitational field. The cluster will never become a stable one! It is curious that if we use two or four balls in our simulations, the cluster becomes more stable.

When we use PUSH_PULL 1, we have unplanned effects. We are not totally sure that these effects are only errors of the program. This is another source of investigation and creation, which may have applications in other areas.

Starting from the program shown in Appendix B, we have adapted the algorithm to simulate a computer virus propagation with a remarkably simple model based on popular knowledge.

Our model has the premises: a) each computer is represented by one ball; b) there are three stages: uninfected, intermediate, and recovered; c) when infected, the computer goes to the intermediate stage, where it stays a time, and then goes to recovered; d) during the intermediate stage, the computer transmits the virus when collides with other that is in the uninfected stage (recovered ones are not able to transmit).

We have altered the "Ball.h", "Ball.cpp", "Globals.h", and "Main.cpp". We started planning to change the "Ball.cpp" because it is there, in each ball object, that the collision is processed when we have a ball with ball collision. The other changes were to complement that major one.

The relevant variables are the global inter_period (Globals.h), which defines the duration time of the intermediate period. The is_virus_simulation (Globals.h) was created to control when the program simulates the "virus" transmission.

Inside the "Ball.h", to be able to be carried by each ball instance, we created the _virus_stage (which is a number standing for the stage) and the _infection_time to control the time since the infection. In the "Ball.cpp", the program will implement the model, set the stage accordingly, and change the stage according to the time since the infection.

The list of options becomes:

```
Please, choose one example or read parameters from a file:
[1] Three balls. (default)
[2] One ball at rest. Piston with gravity.
[3] Eight balls at rest. Piston with gravity.
[4] Fifty balls (gas simulation approximation). Piston with gravity.
[5] Planet and Satellite.
[6] A Fictional Universe.
[7] Five balls computer virus simulation (intermediate period 20s).
[8] Fifty balls computer virus simulation (intermediate period 7s).
[9] Fifty balls computer virus simulation (1/2 speed).
[10] Load parameters from a file.
```

Hence, this shows how the program is flexible and can implement other models with some adaptations. The visual approach of seeing the balls and the ability to alter the program according to what we are researching, added to the parallel computing and C++ execution speed, brings a huge set of creative possibilities.

Please, see in Appendix C the new files, with the new lines in bold and initiated with a "DONE" comment (we had started with "TODO" and changed it to "DONE" after the adaptations). See that we have introduced new parameters in the "Parameters.txt", shown in the same appendix.

Here we have some screenshots:

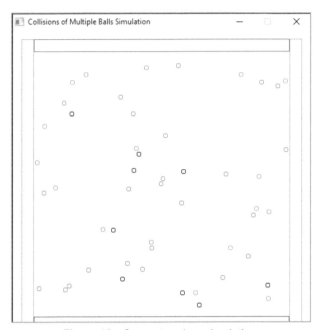

Figure 10 - Computer virus simulation.

In the simulation above, the "non-infected" balls are in black color (default), the "infected" are in red and the "recovered" are in green. We can see that the program is processing the three stages of our model. In the case shown, the intermediate stage time was set to 7.0s and the ball speed to 60 px/s (menu option "8"). What do you think happens when we set the speed to 30 px/s with the same intermediate period?

Figure 11 - Screenshot of simulation: computer virus propagation (beginning).

We have the screen of the beginning of another simulation on the left. In the upper left quadrant, we can observe a ball with red color, being the first ball infected. This is the intermediate stage and lasts a period that can be adjusted.

As the simulation progresses, this ball will collide with others, which will pass into the intermediate stage and will be colored red until the time set to recover has passed, the color changes to green, and the balls no longer spread the "virus" (because these are the chosen premises of the programmed model).

In this specific simulation, surprisingly, some balls have remained uninfected at the end, as their colors are still black, as shown by the figure on the right, but only a few ones.

Nonetheless, as we run the simulation again, we could see another result, showing that there is a random nature in the process.

Nevertheless, the most surprising result was seen comparing several values of the intermediate period. It seems that there is a critical point in the process when the propagation is faster than the recovery. This verification we leave as a challenge for the reader!

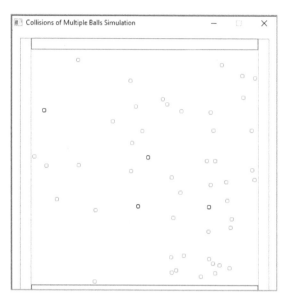

Figure 12 - Screenshot of simulation: computer virus propagation (ending).

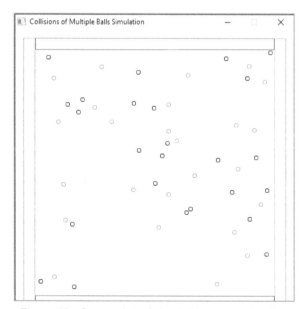

Figure 13 - Screenshot of simulation: computer virus propagation, balls with 1/2 speed (ending).

Trying another approach, applying half of the speed to the balls in relation to the simulation above, we can see on the left that more balls remained uninfected at the end (their colors are still black).

However, because of the randomness of the process, this number was not the same on each try. Despite this, its mean value appeared to be greater compared with the simulation above[7].

This kind of simulation illustrates the possibilities of the program, which can be used as an instrument for learning the programming language and for making simplified simulations, employing together programming and physics.

---

[7] This conclusion has not been submitted to scientific evaluation or validation, but the goal here is just to illustrate the programming potentials.

Concepts addressed

Here is a summary of the programming concepts addressed by the program, taking as reference the code in Appendix A.

Loops, Functions, I/O

We have "resolveCollision()", "circleCircleCollision()", and "squareCircleCollision()" as functions to help the calculation of velocities and positions, as an example of code organization, in the "Ball.cpp". We have "chooseSimulations()", "createObjects()", and "processPiston()" as examples in the 'Main.cpp', about others.

The program reads data from an external file, in the function "loadParametersFromFile()", lines 619-693 in "Main.cpp". The program has a "Menu" with an example of simulations, reading data from the user, in "chooseSimulations()", lines 719-854 of "Main.cpp".

We have an infinite "while-loop" in "main()", lines 101-183, which exits when we close the simulation window. We also have the same kind of loop present at the "Ball::play()", lines 154-400 of "Ball.cpp", and at the "processPiston()", lines 511-611 of "Main.cpp". These loops have a stopwatch and a cycle of a definite time interval in which the computations are processed.

Objected Oriented Programming

The balls, the cylinder's walls, the piston, and the bottom of the cylinder are all objects of some class. Each ball moves based on its function "Ball::play()". Nevertheless, each ball runs on a separate thread; likewise, the piston, which is a "Wall" object and runs in the "processPiston()" function, lines 451-616 of "Main.cpp".

All classes are declared in header ".h" files and implemented in source ".cpp" files, organizing the code.

All classes' data members are specified as "public", "protected", or "private", as we can see in "CylinderObject.h", "Wall.h", and "Ball.h". The member functions are documented through function names and comments, for example, the "Ball" class (declared in "Ball.h").

The cylinder's objects were grouped according to their characteristics. The balls are in movement and have a spherical shape. They are in the "Balls" class. The walls are rectangular. They are in the "Wall" class. Both are derived from the "CylinderObject" class, which has a common characteristic, it has a position, a mass, and can have a speed, as in the case of the piston.

In the "Ball.h" file, we have the "MessageQueue" class (lines 15-27), declared with a template that allows it to accept a generic parameter.

84

Memory Management

In the "createObjects()" function, in line 203 of "Main.cpp", all four parameters (vectors) are passed by reference. This is necessary because the function will create new vector members, updating the content of the parameters.

The program uses "std::shared_ptr" to reference the balls, walls, piston, and bottom, the objects of simulation. As an example, the lines 59-62 of "main()" in the "Main.cpp" file.

The program does not use raw pointers.

Concurrency

Each ball, object of the "Ball" class, runs on a separate thread, as can be viewed starting in line 83 of "Main.cpp", which calls "Ball::simulate" that calls a thread that runs "Ball::play", in line 132 of "Ball.cpp". The threads are stored in a "_threads" vector, which belongs to the "CylinderObject" class. The destructor of the "CylinderObject" sets up a thread barrier before the object is destroyed, calling the "join()" for each thread, in lines 70-71 of the "CylinderObject.cpp".

The class "MessageQueue", declared in the "Ball.h" and implemented at "Ball.cpp", uses as member variables a "std::mutex" and a "std::condition_variable". In the "receive()" method, it uses a "std::unique_lock" to manage the "mutex" and temporally unlock it when inside the "wait()" method of the "condition_variable". This is necessary for the "queue" to be updated. When the "queue" is not empty, so we have new data, the "unique_lock" resumes the lock to get the message from the "queue". The "queue" is used for communications with the "processPiston()", in lines 521-537 of "Main.cpp", through the "Ball::dataIsAvailable" and "Ball::receiveMsg" member functions. It will inform the piston about the ball collisions. The piston will get the information about the velocity and process according to each cycle and time computed to calculate the force that the balls are pushing on it in the "gas mode" simulation.

In the same "processPiston()", another thread is launched with a "lambda" function to print information about the simulation, in lines 471-508.

Real-time simulation

Because of the structure with infinite loops and cycles based on the internal computer clock, we have a real-time simulation, where the computer will try to simulate a physical system at the same rate as the actual clock.

References

[1] R. Sedgewick and K. Wayne, Computer Science: An Interdisciplinary Approach, Boston: Addison-Wesley, 2017, p. Ch. 5.

[2] G. Booch, R. A. Maksimchuk, M. W. Engle, B. J. P. Young, J. Conallen and K. A. Houston, Object-Oriented Analysis and Design with Applications, Addison-Wesley, 2007, p. Ch. 1.1.

[3] Simple DirectMedia Layer, "About SDL," [Online]. Available: https://www.libsdl.org/. [Accessed 2020].

[4] Simple DirectMedia Layer, "Licensing the Simple DirectMedia Layer library," [Online]. Available: https://www.libsdl.org/license.php. [Accessed 29 January 2020].

[5] Halliday, Resnick and Walker, Physics for JEE (Main & Advanced), vol. I, New Delhi: Wiley, 2018, pp. Ch. 9, 310, 311, fig. 9-20, 315.

[6] Halliday and W. Resnick, Physics for JEE (Main & Advanced), vol. II, New Delhi: Wiley, 2018, pp. Ch. 20, 775, fig. 20-4, 776, Ch. 21, 796, fig. 21-1.

[7] Halliday, Resnick and Walker, Physics for JEE (Main & Advanced), vol. I, New Delhi: Wiley, 2018, pp. Ch. 9, p. 322.

[8] F. P. Beer and E. R. Johnston Jr., Mecânica Vetorial para Engenheiros: Dinâmica [Vector Mechanics for Engineers: Dynamics], vol. II, São Paulo: McGraw-Hill do Brasil, 1980, pp. p. 167, solved problem 13.13.

[9] Halliday, Resnick and Walker, Physics for JEE (Main & Advanced), vol. I, New Delhi: Wiley, 2018, pp. Ch. 13, 512, Eq. 13-37.

[10] Canonical Ltd., "Ubuntu," [Online]. Available: https://ubuntu.com/. [Accessed 2019].

[11] Microsoft Corporation, "Visual Studio," [Online]. Available: https://visualstudio.microsoft.com/. [Accessed 2019].

[12] cplusplus.com, "Tutorials: C++ Language," [Online]. Available: https://www.cplusplus.com/doc/tutorial/. [Accessed 2019].

[13] B. Stroustrup, A Tour of C++, 2nd ed., Boston: Addison-Wesley, 2018.

[14] B. Stroustrup, Programming: Principles and Practice Using C++, 2nd ed., Upper Saddle River, NJ: Addison-Wesley, 2014.

[15] Y. Kanetkar, Understanding Pointers In C & C++, fifth revised and updated ed., New Delhi: BPB Publications, 2019.

[16] B. W. Kernighan and D. M. Ritchie, The C Programming Language, 2nd ed., Englewood Cliffs, New Jersey: Prentice-Hall, 1988.

[17] M. Tewfiq, "Capstone Project: Elastic Collisions of Multiple Balls Simulation," 2019. [Online]. Available: https://github.com/marcotf-git/cpp. [Accessed 2019].

Appendix A

Constants.h

```
1  #ifndef CONSTANTS_H
2  #define CONSTANTS_H
3
4  // Screen dimension constants
5  const double SCREEN_WIDTH = 480;
6  const double SCREEN_HEIGHT = 480;
7
8  // cylinder position and dimensions
9  const double CYLINDER_CENTER_POSITION_X = SCREEN_WIDTH / 2;
10 const double CYLINDER_CENTER_POSITION_Y = SCREEN_HEIGHT / 2;
11 const double CYLINDER_WIDTH = SCREEN_WIDTH / 2;
12 const double CYLINDER_HEIGHT = int(SCREEN_HEIGHT * 0.80);
13
14 // wall width
15 const double WALL_WIDTH = 20;
16
17 #endif
18
```

```
 1  // Simulation mode
 2  double gas_mode = 0;
 3
 4  // Ball
 5  double nballs = 8;                  // 100 max. approx.
 6  double ball_radius = 8;             // max 0.5 * WALL_WIDTH approx.
 7  double ball_speed = 0;              // pixels/s (SPPED < RADIUS * 200 max. approx.)
 8  double ball_mass = 0.2;            // 0.01 * piston_mass min approx.
 9  double ball_gravity = 0;           // if zero, simulate gas
10
11  double is_testing = 0;
12  double ball0_speed = 10;           // it will replace the random generated numbers
13  double ball0_vel_angle = 0;
14  double ball1_speed = 10;
15  double ball1_vel_angle = -180;
16
17  // Piston
18  double piston_mass = 10.0;
19  double piston_gravity = 10.0;      // if zero, piston stops
20
21  // Bottom
22  double bottom_temp_min = 0.0;
23  double bottom_temp_max = 100.0;
24
```

```
 1  #ifndef CylinderObject_H
 2  #define CylinderObject_H
 3
 4  #include <vector>
 5  #include <thread>
 6  #include <mutex>
 7
 8  enum class ObjectType
 9  {
10      noObject,
11      objectBall,
12      objectWall,
13  };
14
15  class CylinderObject
16  {
17  public:
18      // constructor / destructor
19      CylinderObject();
20      ~CylinderObject();
21
22      // getters / setters
23      int getID() { return _id; };
24      // position of object on canvas (Ball, Wall, or Piston)
25      void setPosition(double x, double y);
26      void getPosition(double& x, double& y);
27      // velocity of object
28      void setVelocity(double velX, double velY);
29      void getVelocity(double& velX, double& velY);
30      // speed of object
31      double getSpeed();
32      // mass of object
33      void setMass(double m);
34      double getMass();
35      ObjectType getType() { return _type; }
36
37      // typical behavior methods
38      virtual void simulate() {};         // This will be implemented by the Ball class
39
40  protected:
41      // member attributes
42      ObjectType _type;                   // identifies the class type
43      int _id;                            // every cylinder object has its own id
44      double _posX, _posY;                // object position in pixels (center)
45      double _velX, _velY, _speed;        // velocity and speed in pixels/s
46      double _mass;                       // object mass
47
48      std::vector<std::thread> _threads;  // holds all threads that have been launched
49                                          // within this object
50      std::mutex _mutex;                  // mutex to protect member attributes
51      static std::mutex _mtxCout;         // mutex shared by all cylinder objects for
```

```cpp
52      // protecting cout
53  private:
54      // member attributes
55      static int _idCnt;                  // global variable for counting ids
56
57  };
58
59  #endif
60
```

Ball.h

```cpp
1   #ifndef BALL_H
2   #define BALL_H
3
4   #include <mutex>
5   #include <deque>
6   #include <condition_variable>
7
8   #include "CylinderObject.h"
9   #include "Constants.h"
10
11  // forward declarations to avoid including cycle
12  class Wall;
13
14  // This is a message queue class for sending messages between threads
15  template <typename T>
16  class MessageQueue
17  {
18  public:
19      T receive();
20      void send(T&& msg);
21      int getSize();
22
23  private:
24      std::mutex _mutex;
25      std::condition_variable _cond;
26      std::deque<T> _queue;
27  };
28
29  enum class CollisionType {
30      wallCollision,
31      bottomCollision,
32      pistonCollision,
33  };
34
35  struct CollisionData {
36      CollisionType type;
37      double velY;
38  };
39
40  class Ball : public CylinderObject, public std::enable_shared_from_this<Ball>
41  {
42  public:
43      // constructor / destructor
44      Ball();
45
46      // getters / setters
47      void setWalls(std::vector<std::shared_ptr<Wall>> walls) { _walls = walls; }
48      void setBalls(std::vector<std::shared_ptr<Ball>> balls) { _balls = balls; }
49
50      void setRadius(double r) { _radius = r; }
51      double getRadius() { return _radius; }
```

```cpp
52
53      // This method will set a direction, calculating Vx and Vy based on speed and angle
54      void setSpecificDirection(double speed, double angle);
55
56      // This method will choose a random direction for the ball
57      void setRandomDirection(double speed);
58
59      void setGravity(double ball_gravity) { _ball_gravity = ball_gravity;  }
60      void setGasMode(bool gas_mode) { _gas_mode = gas_mode;  }
61
62      // typical behaviour methods
63      bool dataIsAvailable();        // inform that there is a message from other thread
64      CollisionData receiveMsg();    // receive msg from other thread (msg stored in queue)
65      void simulate();              // process ball movements
66      void setShutdown();           // set the flag to exit while-loop in simulate()
67
68      // miscellaneous
69      std::shared_ptr<Ball> get_shared_this() { return shared_from_this(); }
70
71  private:
72      // typical behaviour methods
73      void play();
74      // check if has collided with a wall
75      bool checkWallCollision(double nextX, double nextY, std::shared_ptr<Wall> wall);
76      // check if has collided with another ball
77      bool checkBallCollision(double nextX, double nextY, std::shared_ptr<Ball> ball);
78      // receive direct message to shutdown (exit while-loop)
79      bool getShutdown();
80
81      // member attributes
82      double _radius;                  // ball radius
83      double _ball_gravity;            // gravity
84      bool _gas_mode;                  // simulation mode
85      std::vector<std::shared_ptr<Wall>> _walls;  // walls of cylinder on which ball is on
86      std::vector<std::shared_ptr<Ball>> _balls;  // balls of cylinder on which ball is on
87
88      MessageQueue<CollisionData> _msgQueue;       // msg queue for communications with main
89      std::mutex _mutex;
90
91      bool _shutDown;          // ask ball to end simulation
92  };
93
94  #endif
95
```

```cpp
1  #ifndef WALL_H
2  #define WALL_H
3
4  #include "CylinderObject.h"
5
6  enum class WallType
7  {
8      lateral,
9      piston,
10     bottom,
11 };
12
13 class Wall : public CylinderObject, public std::enable_shared_from_this<Wall>
14 {
15 public:
16     // constructor / destructor
17     Wall();
18
19     // getters / setters
20     // size (width and height)
21     void setSize(double w, double h);
22     void getSize(double& w, double& h);
23     // heat or temperature
24     void setHeat(double ht);
25     double getHeat();
26     // type of the wall: lateral, piston, bottom
27     void setWallType(WallType type) { _wallType = type; }
28     WallType getWallType() { return _wallType; }
29
30     // miscellaneous
31     std::shared_ptr<Wall> get_shared_this() { return shared_from_this(); }
32
33 private:
34
35     // member attributes
36     double _width, _height;     // object width and height in pixels
37     double _temp;               // wall temperature
38     WallType _wallType;         // wall type
39 };
40
41
42 #endif
43
```

```cpp
1   #include <algorithm>
2   #include "CylinderObject.h"
3
4   // init static variables
5   int CylinderObject::_idCnt = 0;
6   std::mutex CylinderObject::_mtxCout;
7
8   CylinderObject::CylinderObject()
9   {
10      _type = ObjectType::noObject;
11      _id = _idCnt;
12      _posX = 0;
13      _posY = 0;
14      _velX = 0;
15      _velY = 0;
16      _speed = 0;
17      _mass = 0;
18      _idCnt++;
19  }
20
21  void CylinderObject::setPosition(double x, double y)
22  {
23      std::lock_guard<std::mutex> lock(_mutex);
24      _posX = x;
25      _posY = y;
26  }
27
28  void  CylinderObject::getPosition(double& x, double& y)
29  {
30      std::lock_guard<std::mutex> lock(_mutex);
31      x = _posX;
32      y = _posY;
33  }
34
35  void CylinderObject::setVelocity(double velX, double velY)
36  {
37      std::lock_guard<std::mutex> lock(_mutex);
38      _velX = velX;
39      _velY = velY;
40      _speed = sqrt(pow(velX, 2) + pow(velY, 2));
41  }
42
43  void CylinderObject::getVelocity(double& velX, double& velY)
44  {
45      std::lock_guard<std::mutex> lock(_mutex);
46      velX = _velX;
47      velY = _velY;
48  }
49
50  double CylinderObject::getSpeed()
51  {
```

```cpp
52        std::lock_guard<std::mutex> lock(_mutex);
53        _speed = sqrt(pow(_velX, 2) + pow(_velY, 2));
54        return _speed;
55    }
56
57    void CylinderObject::setMass(double mass)
58    {
59        _mass = mass;
60    }
61
62    double CylinderObject::getMass()
63    {
64        return _mass;
65    }
66
67    CylinderObject::~CylinderObject()
68    {
69        // set up thread barrier before this object is destroyed
70        std::for_each(_threads.begin(), _threads.end(), [](std::thread& t) {
71            t.join();
72        });
73    }
74
```

```
1  #include <iostream>
2  #include <thread>
3  #include <future>
4  #include <memory>
5  #include <random>
6  #include <algorithm>
7  #include <cmath>
8  #include <array>
9
10 #include "Wall.h"
11 #include "Ball.h"
12
13
14 template <typename T>
15 T MessageQueue<T>::receive()
16 {
17
18     std::unique_lock<std::mutex> uLock(_mutex);     // needs unique_lock because the lock
19     // will be temporarily unlocked inside wait
20     _cond.wait(uLock, [this] { return !_queue.empty(); });     // enter the wait state,
21     // release the lock and resume if new data is available
22
23     T msg = std::move(_queue.back());
24     _queue.pop_back();
25
26     //std::cout << "Message " << msg  << " has been received from the Ball msg queue"
27     // << std::endl;
28
29     return msg;
30 }
31
32 template <typename T>
33 void MessageQueue<T>::send(T&& msg)
34 {
35
36     std::lock_guard<std::mutex> uLock(_mutex);
37
38     //std::cout << "Message " <<  msg << " has been sent to the Ball msg queue"
39     // << std::endl;
40
41     _queue.push_back(std::move(msg));
42     _cond.notify_one();
43
44 }
45
46 template <typename T>
47 int MessageQueue<T>::getSize()
48 {
49     std::lock_guard<std::mutex> uLock(_mutex);
50     return _queue.size();
51 }
```

```
52
53    // helper function declaration
54    double distanceToPoint(double x1, double y1, double x2, double y2);
55    bool squareCircleCollision(double x1, double y1, double w1, double h1,
56                               double x2, double y2, double r2);
57    bool circleCircleCollision(double x1, double y1, double r1,
58                               double x2, double y2, double r2);
59    void resolveCollision(double& posX, double& posY, double& velX, double& velY,
60                          double speed, double mass, double radius,
61                          double& otherX, double& otherY,
62                          double& otherVx, double& otherVy,
63                          double otherSpeed, double otherM, double otherR);
64
65    Ball::Ball()
66    {
67        _type = ObjectType::objectBall;
68        _radius = 0;
69        _velX = 0;
70        _velY = 0;
71        _speed = 0;
72        _shutDown = false;
73        _ball_gravity = 0;
74        _gas_mode = false;
75    }
76
77
78    void Ball::setSpecificDirection(double speed, double angle)
79    {
80        // set velocity
81        double vx, vy;
82        double pi = acos(-1);
83        vx = speed * cos(angle * 2 * pi / 360);
84        vy = -speed * sin(angle * 2 * pi / 360);
85        setVelocity(vx, vy);
86    }
87
88    void Ball::setRandomDirection(double speed)
89    {
90        // pick angle at random and set direction of the ball
91        double angle;
92        std::random_device rd;
93        std::mt19937 generator(rd());
94        std::array<double, 5> intervals{ -60.0, 60.0, 120.0, 240.0, 360.0 };
95        std::array<double, 4> weights{ 1.0, 1.0, 1.0, 1.0 };
96        std::piecewise_constant_distribution<double>
97            distribution(intervals.begin(), intervals.end(), weights.begin());
98        angle = distribution(generator);
99
100       std::cout << "Angle " << angle << std::endl;
101
102       // set velocity
103       setSpecificDirection(speed, angle);
104   }
105
106   bool Ball::dataIsAvailable()
```

```cpp
107  {
108      return (_msgQueue.getSize() > 0);
109  }
110
111  CollisionData Ball::receiveMsg()
112  {
113      return _msgQueue.receive();
114  }
115
116  bool Ball::getShutdown()
117  {
118      return _shutDown;
119  }
120
121  void Ball::setShutdown()
122  {
123      _shutDown = true;
124  }
125
126  // implement the virtual function that will execute a member function into a thread
127  void Ball::simulate()
128  {
129      // Start a thread with the member function "play" and the object "this"
130      // Add the created thread into the _threads vector of parent class (using
131      // emplace_back which means move semantics)
132      _threads.emplace_back(std::thread(&Ball::play, this));
133  }
134
135  // function which is executed in athread
136  void Ball::play()
137  {
138      // print Ball id and thread id
139      std::unique_lock<std::mutex> uLock(_mtxCout);
140      std::cout << "Ball::simulate Ball _id=" << getID() << "  thread id=" <<
141      std::this_thread::get_id() << std::endl;
142      uLock.unlock();
143
144      // initialize variables
145
146      // define cycle duration (to update ball position and check cylinder)
147      int cycleDuration = 10;   // duration of a single simulation cycle in ms
148
149      // init stop watch
150      std::chrono::time_point<std::chrono::system_clock> lastUpdate;
151      lastUpdate = std::chrono::system_clock::now();
152
153      // infinite simulation loop
154      while (!getShutdown())
155      {
156          // compute time difference to stop watch (in ms)
157          auto timeSinceLastUpdate = std::chrono::duration_cast<std::chrono::milliseconds>
158              (std::chrono::system_clock::now() - lastUpdate).count();
159
160          // if past cycle time, update position and check cylinder
161          if (timeSinceLastUpdate >= cycleDuration)
```

```cpp
162          {
163              // reset stop watch for next cycle
164              lastUpdate = std::chrono::system_clock::now();
165
166              // calc next position
167              double velX, velY, nextX, nextY;
168              double posX, posY, dx, dy;
169              getVelocity(velX, velY);
170              getPosition(posX, posY);
171
172              // calc gravity acceleration effect
173              double dVy = _ball_gravity * (timeSinceLastUpdate / 1000.0);   // dVy = Ay*dt
174
175              dx = velX * (timeSinceLastUpdate / 1000.0); // dx = Vx * dt
176              dy = velY * (timeSinceLastUpdate / 1000.0); // dy = Vy * dt
177
178              nextX = posX + dx;
179              nextY = posY + dy;
180
181              // check if ball has reached walls and invert direction
182              bool hasCollidedW = false;
183              bool hasCollidedP = false;
184              bool hasCollidedB = false;
185
186              // process ball with wall collision
187              for (auto wall : _walls) {
188
189                  // process piston->ball elastic collision (the piston moves in y axis):
190                  // m0*v0i + m1*v1i = m0*v0f + m1*v1f
191                  // Ec0i + Ec1i = Ec0f + Ec1f
192                  if (wall->getWallType() == WallType::piston)
193                  {
194
195                      hasCollidedP = (checkWallCollision(nextX, nextY, wall));
196
197                      // if ball is inside the piston: flag the collision
198                      if (hasCollidedP) {
199
200                          //std::cout << "piston-ball colision" << std::endl;
201
202                          double otherVx, otherVy;
203                          wall->getVelocity(otherVx, otherVy);
204                          double x, y, w, h;
205                          wall->getPosition(x, y);
206                          wall->getSize(w, h);
207
208                          double velCollisionGas = velY - otherVy;
209
210                          double otherX, otherY;
211                          otherX = posX;   // like collision with a ball at the same x coordinate
212                          otherY = y;
213
214                          double speed = getSpeed();
215                          double otherSpeed = wall->getSpeed();
216
```

```cpp
217             double mass = _mass;
218             double otherM = wall->getMass();
219
220             double radius = _radius;
221             double otherR = h / 2;      // it is like a collision with a ball
222             // at the same x coordinate, with r = h/2
223
224             resolveCollision(posX, posY, velX, velY, speed, mass, radius,
225                              otherX, otherY, otherVx, otherVy, otherSpeed,
226                              otherM, otherR);
227
228             // Two models of simulation: in the gas mode, the piston is
229             // processed in main
230             if (!(_gas_mode))
231             {
232                 // update positions and velocities
233                 wall->setVelocity(0, otherVy);
234                 wall->setPosition(x, otherY);
235
236                 setVelocity(velX, velY);
237                 setPosition(posX, posY);
238             }
239             else
240             {
241                 // msg to main to update piston:
242                 // F*dt = m0*(v0i-v0f)
243                 // F = m1*a
244                 _msgQueue.send({ CollisionType::pistonCollision,
245                                 velCollisionGas });
246
247                 // update ball position and velocity
248                 // m0*v0i + m1*v1i = m0*v0f + m1*v1f
249                 // Ec0i + Ec1i = Ec0f + Ec1f
250                 setVelocity(velX, velY);
251                 setPosition(posX, posY);
252
253             }
254
255         }
256
257     }
258     else
259     {
260         // process ball with wall and bottom collisions
261         // m0*v0i = m0*v0f
262         hasCollidedW = checkWallCollision(nextX, nextY, wall);
263
264         if (hasCollidedW) {
265             // verify if it has collided with bottom or lateral and send
266             // message to main
267             if (wall->getWallType() == WallType::lateral) {
268                 //std::cout << "ball->lateral collision" << std::endl <<
269                 // std::endl;
270                 _msgQueue.send({ CollisionType::wallCollision, velY });
271             }
```

```
272            else if (wall->getWallType() == WallType::bottom) {
273                //std::cout << "ball->bottom collision" << std::endl <<
274                // std::endl;
275                _msgQueue.send({ CollisionType::bottomCollision, velY });
276            }
277        }
278
279
280        // if there is a collision, change ball direction
281        if (hasCollidedW) {
282
283            double x, y;
284            wall->getPosition(x, y);
285
286            // if it has collided in dx, set x component of velocity
287            if (checkWallCollision(nextX, posY, wall))
288            {
289                if (posX < x) { // the wall is in front
290                    velX = -abs(velX);
291                }
292                else { // the wall is behind
293                    velX = abs(velX);
294                }
295
296            }
297            // if it has collided in dy, set y component of velocity
298            if (checkWallCollision(posX, nextY, wall))
299            {
300                if (posY > y) {  // the wall is behind
301                    velY = abs(velY);
302                }
303                else {    // the wall is in front
304                    velY = -abs(velY);
305
306                }
307
308                // Adjust ball vel. to approx. temperature effect of bottom
309                if (wall->getWallType() == WallType::bottom) {
310                    if (abs(velY) < 1.0 * wall->getHeat())
311                    {
312                        velY = -1.0 * wall->getHeat();
313                    }
314                }
315            }
316
317            // update velocity
318            setVelocity(velX, velY);
319
320            // update position
321            setPosition(nextX, nextY);
322
323            break;
324        }
325    }
326
```

```
327
328        } // eof ball-wall collision
329
330
331        // process ball with ball collisions
332        // m0*v0i + m1*v1i = m0*v0f + m1*v1f
333        // Ec0i + Ec1i = Ec0f + Ec1f
334        if (!hasCollidedW && !hasCollidedP)
335        {
336            int thisBallId = getID();
337            for (auto ball : _balls)
338            {
339                int otherBallId = ball->getID();
340                if (thisBallId != otherBallId)
341                {
342                    hasCollidedB = checkBallCollision(nextX, nextY, ball);
343                    //std::cout << "Ball collision id1 " << thisBallId << "  id2 "<<
344                    // otherBallId << std::endl;
345                    //std::this_thread::sleep_for(std::chrono::milliseconds(3000));
346
347                    // if there is a collision, change ball direction (elastic
348                    // collision)
349                    if (hasCollidedB) {
350
351                        double otherX, otherY;
352                        ball->getPosition(otherX, otherY);
353
354                        double otherVx, otherVy;
355                        ball->getVelocity(otherVx, otherVy);
356
357                        double speed = getSpeed();
358                        double otherSpeed = ball->getSpeed();
359
360                        double mass = getMass();
361                        double otherM = ball->getMass();
362
363                        double radius = getRadius();
364                        double otherR = ball->getRadius();
365
366                        resolveCollision(posX, posY, velX, velY,
367                                         speed, mass, radius,
368                                         otherX, otherY, otherVx, otherVy,
369                                         otherSpeed, otherM, otherR);
370
371                        // update velocities
372                        setVelocity(velX, velY + dVy);
373                        ball->setVelocity(otherVx, otherVy);
374
375                        // update positions
376                        setPosition(posX, posY);
377                        ball->setPosition(otherX, otherY);
378
379                        break;
380                    }
381                }
```

```
382                         }
383
384                     } // eof new ball-ball collision
385
386
387                     // if has not collided, just update position and velocity
388                     if (!hasCollidedW && !hasCollidedB && !hasCollidedP)
389                     {
390                         setPosition(nextX, nextY);
391                         setVelocity(velX, velY + dVy);
392                     }
393
394
395             } // eof cycle
396
397             // sleep at every iteration to reduce CPU usage
398             std::this_thread::sleep_for(std::chrono::milliseconds(1));
399
400         } // eof simulation loop
401
402 }
403
404 // Verify and process the collision of the ball with the cylinder walls
405 bool Ball::checkWallCollision(double nextX, double nextY, std::shared_ptr<Wall> wall)
406 {
407     double x, y, w, h;
408     bool collision = false;
409
410     wall->getPosition(x, y);
411     wall->getSize(w, h);
412     collision = squareCircleCollision(x, y, w, h, nextX, nextY, _radius);
413
414     return collision;
415 }
416
417 // Verify and process the collision of the ball with the cylinder walls
418 bool Ball::checkBallCollision(double nextX, double nextY, std::shared_ptr<Ball> ball)
419 {
420     double x, y, r;
421     bool collision = false;
422
423     ball->getPosition(x, y);
424     r = ball->getRadius();
425     collision = circleCircleCollision(nextX, nextY, _radius, x, y, r);
426
427     return collision;
428 }
429
430 // verify collision between square x1,y1,w1,h1 and circle x2,y2,r2
431 bool squareCircleCollision(double x1, double y1, double w1, double h1,
432                             double x2, double y2, double r2)
433 {
434     double closestX, closestY;
435     bool collision = false;
436
```

```
437         // find the closest x coordinate of the wall to the circle
438         if (x1 + w1 * 0.5 < x2 - r2) { closestX = x1 + w1 * 0.5; }
439         else if (x1 - w1 * 0.5 > x2 + r2) { closestX = x1 - w1 * 0.5; }
440         else { closestX = x2; }
441
442         // find the closest y coordinate of the wall to the circle
443         if (y1 + h1 * 0.5 < y2 - r2) { closestY = y1 + h1 * 0.5; }
444         else if (y1 - h1 * 0.5 > y2 + r2) { closestY = y1 - h1 * 0.5; }
445         else { closestY = y2; }
446
447         if (distanceToPoint(x2, y2, closestX, closestY) < r2) {
448             collision = true;
449         }
450
451         return collision;
452     }
453
454     // verify collision between circle x1,y1,r1 and circle x2,y2,r2
455     bool circleCircleCollision(double x1, double y1, double r1,
456                                double x2, double y2, double r2)
457     {
458         double distance;
459         bool collision;
460
461         distance = distanceToPoint(x1, y1, x2, y2);
462         collision = (distance < (r1 + r2));
463
464         return collision;
465     }
466
467     double distanceToPoint(double x1, double y1, double x2, double y2)
468     {
469         double distance;
470
471         distance = sqrt(pow(x1 - x2, 2.0) + pow(y1 - y2, 2.0));
472
473         return distance;
474     }
475
476     // resolve collision elastic
477     void resolveCollision(double& posX, double& posY, double& velX, double& velY,
478                           double speed, double mass, double radius,
479                           double& otherX, double& otherY, double& otherVx, double& otherVy,
480                           double otherSpeed, double otherM, double otherR)
481     {
482
483         if (mass == 0 || otherM == 0)
484         {
485             std::cout << "Error: mass is zero!" << std::endl;
486             return;
487         }
488
489         double angleCol = atan2(otherY - posY, otherX - posX);
490         double direction = atan2(velY, velX);
491         double otherDirection = atan2(otherVy, otherVx);
```

```
492
493     double new_xspeed = speed * cos(direction - angleCol);
494     double new_yspeed = speed * sin(direction - angleCol);
495
496     double new_xspeedOther = otherSpeed * cos(otherDirection - angleCol);
497     double new_yspeedOther = otherSpeed * sin(otherDirection - angleCol);
498
499     double final_xspeed = ((mass - otherM) * new_xspeed +
500         (otherM + otherM) * new_xspeedOther) / (mass + otherM);
501     double final_xspeedOther = ((mass + mass) * new_xspeed +
502         (otherM - mass) * new_xspeedOther) / (mass + otherM);
503     double final_yspeed = new_yspeed;
504     double final_yspeedOther = new_yspeedOther;
505
506     double cosAngle = cos(angleCol);
507     double sinAngle = sin(angleCol);
508
509     double newVelX, newVelY;
510     newVelX = cosAngle * final_xspeed - sinAngle * final_yspeed;
511     newVelY = sinAngle * final_xspeed + cosAngle * final_yspeed;
512
513     double newOtherVelX, newOtherVelY;
514     newOtherVelX = cosAngle * final_xspeedOther - sinAngle * final_yspeedOther;
515     newOtherVelY = sinAngle * final_xspeedOther + cosAngle * final_yspeedOther;
516
517     // get the minimum translation distance to push balls apart after intersecting
518     struct Position {
519         double x;
520         double y;
521         double length() {
522             return sqrt(pow(x, 2.0) + pow(y, 2.0));
523         }
524     } pos1, pos2, posDiff, mtd;
525
526     pos1.x = posX;
527     pos1.y = posY;
528     pos2.x = otherX;
529     pos2.y = otherY;
530     posDiff.x = pos1.x - pos2.x;
531     posDiff.y = pos1.y - pos2.y;
532
533     double d = posDiff.length();
534     double k = (((radius + otherR) - d) / d);
535     mtd.x = posDiff.x * k;
536     mtd.y = posDiff.y * k;
537
538     double im = 1 / mass;
539     double imOther = 1 / otherM;
540
541     // push-pull them apart based off their mass
542     pos1.x = pos1.x + mtd.x * (im / (im + imOther));
543     pos1.y = pos1.y + mtd.y * (im / (im + imOther));
544     pos2.x = pos2.x - mtd.x * (imOther / (im + imOther));
545     pos2.y = pos2.y - mtd.y * (imOther / (im + imOther));
546
```

```
547      // Process ball with wall collision generated by the pushing balls apart
548      if ((pos1.x + radius >= CYLINDER_CENTER_POSITION_X + CYLINDER_WIDTH / 2) ||
549          (pos1.x - radius <= CYLINDER_CENTER_POSITION_X - CYLINDER_WIDTH / 2))
550      {
551          newVelX = -1.0 * newVelX;
552      }
553
554      if ((pos1.y + radius >= CYLINDER_CENTER_POSITION_Y + CYLINDER_HEIGHT / 2) ||
555          (pos1.y - radius <= CYLINDER_CENTER_POSITION_Y - CYLINDER_HEIGHT / 2))
556      {
557          newVelY = -1.0 * newVelY;
558      }
559
560      if ((pos2.x + otherR >= CYLINDER_CENTER_POSITION_X + CYLINDER_WIDTH / 2) ||
561          (pos2.x - otherR <= CYLINDER_CENTER_POSITION_X - CYLINDER_WIDTH / 2))
562      {
563          newOtherVelX = -1.0 * newOtherVelX;
564      }
565
566      if ((pos2.y + otherR >= CYLINDER_CENTER_POSITION_Y + CYLINDER_HEIGHT / 2) ||
567          (pos2.y - otherR <= CYLINDER_CENTER_POSITION_Y - CYLINDER_HEIGHT / 2))
568      {
569          newOtherVelY = -1.0 * newOtherVelY;
570      }
571
572      velX = newVelX;
573      velY = newVelY;
574
575      posX = pos1.x;
576      posY = pos1.y;
577
578      otherVx = newOtherVelX;
579      otherVy = newOtherVelY;
580
581      otherX = pos2.x;
582      otherY = pos2.y;
583
584  }
585
```

```
1  #include "Wall.h"
2
3  Wall::Wall()
4  {
5      _type = ObjectType::objectWall;
6      _wallType = WallType::lateral;
7      _width = 0;
8      _height = 0;
9      _temp = 0;
10 }
11
12 void  Wall::setSize(double w, double h)
13 {
14     _width = w;
15     _height = h;
16 }
17
18 void  Wall::getSize(double& w, double& h)
19 {
20     w = _width;
21     h = _height;
22 }
23
24 void Wall::setHeat(double ht)
25 {
26     std::lock_guard<std::mutex> lock(_mutex);
27     _temp = ht;
28 }
29
30 double Wall::getHeat()
31 {
32     std::lock_guard<std::mutex> lock(_mutex);
33     return _temp;
34 }
35
```

```cpp
1  #include <iostream>
2  #include <iomanip>
3  #include <fstream>
4  #include <string>
5  #include <thread>
6  #include <vector>
7  #include <array>
8  #include <random>
9  #include <time.h>
10 #include <vector>
11 #include <SDL2/SDL.h>
12
13 #include "Constants.h"
14 #include "Globals.h"
15 #include "Ball.h"
16 #include "Wall.h"
17
18
19 // The window we will be rendering to
20 std::shared_ptr<SDL_Window> gWindow = nullptr;
21
22 // The window renderer
23 std::shared_ptr<SDL_Renderer> gRenderer = nullptr;
24
25 // Start up SDL and create window
26 bool initRenderer();
27
28 // Free media and shut down SDL
29 void closeRenderer();
30
31 // Draw circle using midpoint circle algorithm
32 void drawCircle(std::shared_ptr<SDL_Renderer> gRenderer,
33                 int32_t centreX, int32_t centreY, int32_t radius);
34
35 // Load parameters from a file
36 bool chooseSimulations();
37 bool loadParametersFromFile();
38 void printParameters();
39
40 // Create objects;
41 void createObjects(std::vector<std::shared_ptr<Wall>>& walls,
42                    std::shared_ptr<Wall>& piston, std::shared_ptr<Wall>& bottom,
43                    std::vector<std::shared_ptr<Ball>>& balls);
44
45 // Render objects
46 void renderBall(std::shared_ptr<Ball> ball);
47 void renderWalls(std::vector<std::shared_ptr<Wall>> walls);
48
49 // Piston dynamics
50 void processPiston(std::shared_ptr<Wall> piston, std::shared_ptr<Wall> bottom,
51     std::vector<std::shared_ptr<Ball>> balls, bool& finish);
```

```
52
53
54   /* Main function */
55   int main(int argc, char* args[]) // needs argc and args[] for the SDL
56   {
57
58       // Simulation objects
59       std::vector<std::shared_ptr<Wall>> walls;
60       std::shared_ptr<Wall> piston;
61       std::shared_ptr<Wall> bottom;
62       std::vector<std::shared_ptr<Ball>> balls;
63
64       // Choose simulations
65       if (!chooseSimulations())
66           return 0;
67
68       // create the objects
69       createObjects(walls, piston, bottom, balls);
70
71       if(balls.size() >= 1 && is_testing > 0)
72       balls.at(0)->setSpecificDirection(ball0_speed, ball0_vel_angle); // set for testing
73
74       if(balls.size() >= 2 && is_testing > 0)
75       balls.at(1)->setSpecificDirection(ball1_speed, ball1_vel_angle); // set for testing
76
77       // msg for stopping the threads
78       bool finish = false;
79
80       // simulate
81       for (auto ball : balls)
82       {
83           ball->simulate();
84       }
85
86       // process piston dynamics
87       std::thread t1(processPiston, piston, bottom, std::ref(balls), std::ref(finish));
88
89       // Start up SDL and create window
90       if (!initRenderer())
91       {
92           std::cout << "Failed to initialize!" << std::endl;
93       }
94       else
95       {
96           // initialize variables
97           bool quit = false; // loop flag
98           int tempKey = 0;
99
100          // Main loop
101          while (!quit)
102          {
103
104              SDL_Event e; // Event handler
105
106              // Handle keycylinder events on queue
```

```cpp
107            while (SDL_PollEvent(&e) != 0)
108            {
109                // User requests quit
110                if (e.type == SDL_QUIT)
111                {
112                    quit = true;
113                }
114
115                // adjust temp at bottom
116                if (e.type == SDL_KEYDOWN && e.key.repeat == 0)
117                {
118                    switch (e.key.keysym.sym)
119                    {
120                    case SDLK_LEFT:
121                        tempKey = -1;
122                        break;
123                    case SDLK_RIGHT:
124                        tempKey = +1;
125                        break;
126                    default:
127                        break;
128                    }
129                }
130
131                if (e.type == SDL_KEYUP && e.key.repeat == 0)
132                {
133                    switch (e.key.keysym.sym)
134                    {
135                    case SDLK_LEFT:
136                        if(tempKey < 0)
137                            tempKey = 0;
138                        break;
139                    case SDLK_RIGHT:
140                        if(tempKey > 0)
141                            tempKey = 0;
142                        break;
143                    default:
144                        break;
145                    }
146                }
147
148            }
149
150        // update temp
151        if (tempKey == +1) {
152            double temp = bottom->getHeat();
153            if (temp < bottom_temp_max) {
154                temp++;
155                bottom->setHeat(temp);
156            }
157        }
158        if (tempKey == -1) {
159            double temp = bottom->getHeat();
160            if (temp > bottom_temp_min) {
161                temp--;
```

```cpp
162                    bottom->setHeat(temp);
163                }
164            }
165
166            // Clear screen
167            SDL_SetRenderDrawColor(gRenderer.get(), 0xFF, 0xFF, 0xFF, 0xFF);
168            SDL_RenderClear(gRenderer.get());
169
170            // Render ball
171            for (auto ball : balls)
172            {
173                renderBall(ball);
174            }
175
176            // Render walls
177            renderWalls(walls);
178
179            // Update screen
180            SDL_RenderPresent(gRenderer.get());
181
182
183        } // eof main loop
184
185    }
186
187    // close renderer
188    closeRenderer();
189
190    // ask ball:simulate to terminate
191    for (auto ball : balls) {
192        ball->setShutdown();
193    }
194
195    // wait for threads before returning
196    finish = true;
197    t1.join();
198
199    return 0;
200 }
201
202
203 void createObjects(std::vector<std::shared_ptr<Wall>>& walls,
204                    std::shared_ptr<Wall>& piston, std::shared_ptr<Wall>& bottom,
205                    std::vector<std::shared_ptr<Ball>>& balls)
206 {
207    // create walls
208    for (int nw = 0; nw < 4; nw++)
209    {
210        walls.push_back(std::make_shared<Wall>());
211    }
212
213    // lateral walls
214    walls.at(0)->setPosition(CYLINDER_CENTER_POSITION_X - CYLINDER_WIDTH / 2,
215                             CYLINDER_CENTER_POSITION_Y);
216    walls.at(0)->setSize(WALL_WIDTH, CYLINDER_HEIGHT + WALL_WIDTH);
```

```cpp
217    walls.at(0)->setWallType(WallType::lateral);
218
219    walls.at(1)->setPosition(CYLINDER_CENTER_POSITION_X + CYLINDER_WIDTH / 2,
220                             CYLINDER_CENTER_POSITION_Y);
221    walls.at(1)->setSize(WALL_WIDTH, CYLINDER_HEIGHT + WALL_WIDTH);
222    walls.at(1)->setWallType(WallType::lateral);
223
224    // piston and bottom walls
225    walls.at(2)->setPosition(CYLINDER_CENTER_POSITION_X,
226                             CYLINDER_CENTER_POSITION_Y - CYLINDER_HEIGHT / 2);
227    walls.at(2)->setSize(CYLINDER_WIDTH - WALL_WIDTH, WALL_WIDTH);
228    walls.at(2)->setWallType(WallType::piston);
229
230    walls.at(3)->setPosition(CYLINDER_CENTER_POSITION_X,
231                             CYLINDER_CENTER_POSITION_Y + CYLINDER_HEIGHT / 2);
232    walls.at(3)->setSize(CYLINDER_WIDTH - WALL_WIDTH, WALL_WIDTH);
233    walls.at(3)->setWallType(WallType::bottom);
234
235    // create reference to piston
236    piston = walls.at(2);
237    piston->setMass(piston_mass);
238
239    // create reference to bottom
240    bottom = walls.at(3);
241    bottom->setHeat(bottom_temp_min);
242
243    // create cells into the cylinder
244    int nCells = 0;          // calc number of cells
245    int nRows, nCols;
246    for (int n = 1; n <= nballs; n++)
247    {
248        nCells = n * n;
249        nRows = n;
250        nCols = n;
251        if (nCells >= nballs)
252        {
253            break;
254        }
255    }
256
257    struct Cell {
258        double x, y;
259    };
260
261    std::vector<Cell> places;
262    double inicX, inicY, aux;
263    walls.at(0)->getPosition(inicX, aux);
264    inicX += WALL_WIDTH * 0.5;
265    walls.at(2)->getPosition(aux, inicY);
266    inicY += WALL_WIDTH * 0.5;
267
268    for (int nc = 0; nc < nCells; nc++)
269    {
270        Cell cell;
271        cell.x = (inicX)+(nc % nCols) * ((CYLINDER_WIDTH - WALL_WIDTH) / nCols) +
```

```
272                 ((CYLINDER_WIDTH - WALL_WIDTH) / nCols) / 2.0;
273             cell.y = (inicY)+(nc / nCols) * ((CYLINDER_HEIGHT - WALL_WIDTH) / nRows) +
274                 ((CYLINDER_HEIGHT - WALL_WIDTH) / nRows) / 2.0;
275             places.push_back(cell);
276         }
277
278         // create balls at the cells
279         for (int nb = 0; nb < nballs; nb++)
280         {
281             balls.push_back(std::make_shared<Ball>());
282             balls.at(nb)->setPosition(places.at(nb).x, places.at(nb).y);
283
284             // prevent ball size overflow
285             if (nCols * 2.0 * ball_radius > CYLINDER_WIDTH * 0.98) {
286                 balls.at(nb)->setRadius(CYLINDER_WIDTH * 0.98 / nCols / 2.0);
287             }
288             else {
289                 balls.at(nb)->setRadius(ball_radius);
290             }
291
292             balls.at(nb)->setRandomDirection(ball_speed);
293             balls.at(nb)->setMass(ball_mass);
294             balls.at(nb)->setGravity(ball_gravity);
295             balls.at(nb)->setGasMode((gas_mode > 0));
296         }
297
298         // set the reference to other balls and walls into each ball
299         for (auto ball : balls)
300         {
301             ball->setBalls(balls);
302             ball->setWalls(walls);
303         }
304 }
305
306 bool initRenderer()
307 {
308     // Initialization flag
309     bool success = true;
310
311     // Initialize SDL
312     if (SDL_Init(SDL_INIT_VIDEO) < 0)
313     {
314         std::cout << "SDL could not initialize! SDL Error: " << SDL_GetError() <<
315             std::endl;
316         success = false;
317     }
318     else
319     {
320         // Create window
321         gWindow = std::shared_ptr<SDL_Window>
322             (SDL_CreateWindow("Elastic Collisions of Multiple Balls Simulation",
323                 SDL_WINDOWPOS_UNDEFINED, SDL_WINDOWPOS_UNDEFINED,
324                 SCREEN_WIDTH, SCREEN_HEIGHT, SDL_WINDOW_SHOWN),
325                 SDL_DestroyWindow);
326         if (gWindow == nullptr)
```

```
327            {
328                std::cout << "Window could not be created! SDL Error: " << SDL_GetError() <<
329                    std::endl;
330                success = false;
331            }
332        else
333            {
334                // Create vsynced renderer for window
335                gRenderer = std::shared_ptr<SDL_Renderer>
336                    (SDL_CreateRenderer(gWindow.get(),
337                        -1, SDL_RENDERER_ACCELERATED | SDL_RENDERER_PRESENTVSYNC),
338                        SDL_DestroyRenderer);
339                if (gRenderer == NULL) {
340                    std::cout << "Renderer could not be created! SDL Error: " <<
341                        SDL_GetError() << std::endl;
342                    success = false;
343                }
344            else
345                {
346                    // Initialize renderer color
347                    SDL_SetRenderDrawColor(gRenderer.get(), 0xFF, 0xFF, 0xFF, 0xFF);
348                }
349            }
350        }
351
352        return success;
353 }
354
355 void closeRenderer() {
356        // Quit SDL subsystems
357        SDL_Quit();
358 }
359
360 void drawCircle(std::shared_ptr<SDL_Renderer> renderer,
361                int32_t centreX, int32_t centreY, int32_t radius)
362 {
363        const int32_t diameter = (radius * 2);
364
365        int32_t x = (radius - 1);
366        int32_t y = 0;
367        int32_t tx = 1;
368        int32_t ty = 1;
369        int32_t error = (tx - diameter);
370
371        while (x >= y)
372        {
373            //  Each of the following renders an octant of the circle
374            SDL_RenderDrawPoint(renderer.get(), centreX + x, centreY - y);
375            SDL_RenderDrawPoint(renderer.get(), centreX + x, centreY + y);
376            SDL_RenderDrawPoint(renderer.get(), centreX - x, centreY - y);
377            SDL_RenderDrawPoint(renderer.get(), centreX - x, centreY + y);
378            SDL_RenderDrawPoint(renderer.get(), centreX + y, centreY - x);
379            SDL_RenderDrawPoint(renderer.get(), centreX + y, centreY + x);
380            SDL_RenderDrawPoint(renderer.get(), centreX - y, centreY - x);
381            SDL_RenderDrawPoint(renderer.get(), centreX - y, centreY + x);
```

```
382
383        if (error <= 0)
384        {
385            ++y;
386            error += ty;
387            ty += 2;
388        }
389
390        if (error > 0)
391        {
392            --x;
393            tx += 2;
394            error += (tx - diameter);
395        }
396    }
397 }
398
399 void renderBall(std::shared_ptr<Ball> ball)
400 {
401    double x, y, r;
402    ball->getPosition(x, y);
403    r = ball->getRadius();
404
405    if (x < 0) return;
406
407    SDL_SetRenderDrawColor(gRenderer.get(), 0x00, 0x00, 0x00, 0xFF);
408
409    drawCircle(gRenderer, (int32_t) x, (int32_t) y, (int32_t) r);
410
411 }
412
413 void renderWalls(std::vector<std::shared_ptr<Wall>> walls)
414 {
415    for (auto wall : walls) {
416
417        // set the rectangle
418        SDL_Rect rect;
419        double x, y, w, h;
420        wall->getPosition(x, y);
421        wall->getSize(w, h);
422
423        if (x < 0) continue;
424
425        rect.x = int (x - w / 2);
426        rect.y = int (y - h / 2);
427        rect.w = int (w);
428        rect.h = int (h);
429
430        switch (wall->getWallType())
431        {
432            case WallType::lateral:
433                SDL_SetRenderDrawColor(gRenderer.get(), 0x00, 0x00, 0x00, 0xFF);
434                break;
435            case WallType::piston:
436                SDL_SetRenderDrawColor(gRenderer.get(), 0x00, 0x00, 0xFF, 0xFF);
```

```cpp
437                    break;
438             case WallType::bottom:
439                 double k = (wall->getHeat() - bottom_temp_min) /
440                     (bottom_temp_max + 0.001);
441                 double kMin = bottom_temp_min / (bottom_temp_max + 0.001);
442                 uint16_t red = uint16_t(0xFF * 0.60 + (0xFF * kMin + 0xFF * k) * 0.40);
443                 SDL_SetRenderDrawColor(gRenderer.get(), red, 0x00, 0x00, 0xFF);
444                 break;
445         }
446
447         SDL_RenderDrawRect(gRenderer.get(), &rect);
448     }
449 }
450
451 void processPiston(std::shared_ptr<Wall> piston, std::shared_ptr<Wall> bottom,
452     std::vector<std::shared_ptr<Ball>> balls, bool& finish)
453 {
454
455     // Set to piston dynamics
456     long pistoncollisions = 0;
457     double upForce = 0.0;
458     double mv = 0.0;
459     double avgUpForce = 0.0;
460     double downForce = 0.0;     // for testing
461     downForce = piston_gravity * piston_mass;
462     double pistonVel = 0.0;
463     int cycleDuration = 10;   // define cycle duration (ms) to calc up force
464     bool gasMode = (gas_mode > 0);
465     double temp = 0;
466
467     // init stop watch
468     std::chrono::time_point<std::chrono::system_clock> lastUpdate;
469     lastUpdate = std::chrono::system_clock::now();
470
471     auto f0 = [balls, cycleDuration, gasMode, &avgUpForce, &downForce, &temp, &finish]()
472     {
473         long simTime = 0;
474         while (!finish) {
475             std::this_thread::sleep_for(std::chrono::milliseconds(1000));
476             // count balls inside piston (testing)
477             int count = 0;
478             for (auto ball : balls)
479             {
480                 double x, y;
481                 ball->getPosition(x, y);
482                 if (x > CYLINDER_CENTER_POSITION_X - CYLINDER_WIDTH * 0.5 && x <
483                     CYLINDER_CENTER_POSITION_X + CYLINDER_WIDTH * 0.5 &&
484                     y > CYLINDER_CENTER_POSITION_Y - CYLINDER_HEIGHT * 0.5 && y <
485                     CYLINDER_CENTER_POSITION_Y + CYLINDER_HEIGHT * 0.5)
486                 {
487                     count++;
488                 }
489             }
490
491             std::cout << "Time:" << simTime << "\t";
```

```
492        std::cout << "balls:" << count << "     ";
493
494        if (gasMode) {
495            std::cout << "gas avg(1.0s) up force : " << std::fixed <<
496                std::setprecision(2) << abs(avgUpForce) << "  \t";
497            std::cout << "piston down force: " << std::setprecision(2) <<
498                downForce << " \t";
499        }
500
501        std::cout << "~temp(bottom) : " << std::setprecision(2) << temp <<
502            std::endl;
503
504        simTime++;
505    }
506 };
507
508 std::thread t1(f0);          // thread for monitoring and testing
509
510
511 while (!finish)
512 {
513     // compute time difference (in ms)
514         auto timeSinceLastUpdate =
515             std::chrono::duration_cast<std::chrono::milliseconds>
516             (std::chrono::system_clock::now() - lastUpdate).count();
517
518     // Receive and process msg from balls about a collision with the piston
519     for (auto ball : balls)
520     {
521         while (ball->dataIsAvailable())
522         {
523             //std::cout << "Main: ball msg available" << std::endl;
524             CollisionData msg = ball->receiveMsg();
525             CollisionType colType = msg.type;
526             double velocity = msg.velY;     // downward is positve
527             switch (colType) {
528             case CollisionType::bottomCollision:
529                 //std::cout << "ball-bottom collision" << std::endl;
530                 break;
531             case CollisionType::pistonCollision:
532                 //std::cout << "*gas* ball-piston collision" << std::endl;
533                 pistoncollisions++;
534                 mv += 2.0 * ball_mass * velocity;    // force in the piston
535                 break;
536             }
537         }
538     }
539
540
541     // Process piston dymamics
542     if (timeSinceLastUpdate > cycleDuration) {
543
544         // F * t = m * v
545         upForce = mv / (timeSinceLastUpdate / 1000.0);
546         avgUpForce = avgUpForce + upForce / (1000/cycleDuration) - avgUpForce /
```

```
547            (1000/cycleDuration);      // 1000ms average (for printing)
548
549        double posX, posY;
550        double pistonW, pistonH;
551        double velX, velY;
552        double acceleration;
553
554        piston->getPosition(posX, posY);
555        piston->getSize(pistonW, pistonH);
556        piston->getVelocity(velX, velY);
557
558        // F = m * a
559        acceleration = (upForce + downForce) / (piston_mass + 1e-10);  // downward =
560        // positive; prevent overflow
561
562        // calc piston position  (x - x0) = vo * t + 1/2 * a * t^2
563        posY = posY + pistonVel * (timeSinceLastUpdate / 1000.0) +
564            0.5 * acceleration * pow(timeSinceLastUpdate / 1000.0, 2);    // approx;
565
566        // piston velocity for next cycle
567        pistonVel = velY + acceleration * (timeSinceLastUpdate / 1000.0);
568
569        // Limit piston movement inside cylinder area
570        if (posY < CYLINDER_CENTER_POSITION_Y - CYLINDER_HEIGHT * 0.5)
571        {
572            posY = CYLINDER_CENTER_POSITION_Y - CYLINDER_HEIGHT * 0.5;
573
574        }
575        else if ((posY > CYLINDER_CENTER_POSITION_Y +
576            CYLINDER_HEIGHT * 0.5 - WALL_WIDTH))
577        {
578            posY = CYLINDER_CENTER_POSITION_Y +
579                CYLINDER_HEIGHT * 0.5 - WALL_WIDTH;
580        }
581
582        // piston at the top: no velocity upward
583        if (posY <= (CYLINDER_CENTER_POSITION_Y - CYLINDER_HEIGHT * 0.5))
584        {
585            if (pistonVel < 0) pistonVel = 0;
586        }
587        // piston at the bottom: no velocity downward
588        else if (posY >= (CYLINDER_CENTER_POSITION_Y +
589            CYLINDER_HEIGHT * 0.5 - WALL_WIDTH))
590        {
591            if (pistonVel > 0) pistonVel = -pistonVel;
592        }
593
594        // update piston
595        piston->setPosition(posX, posY);
596        piston->setVelocity(0.0, pistonVel);
597
598        // reset for next cycle
599        pistoncollisions = 0;
600        mv = 0.0;
601        temp = bottom->getHeat();
```

```
602
603                // reset stop watch for next cycle
604                lastUpdate = std::chrono::system_clock::now();
605
606            } // eof cycle computations
607
608            // sleep at every iteration to reduce CPU usage
609            std::this_thread::sleep_for(std::chrono::milliseconds(1));
610
611        } // eof while loop
612
613
614        t1.join(); // it will close because it is monitoring the finish flag
615
616 }
617
618
619 bool loadParametersFromFile()
620 {
621
622     struct Reading {
623         std::string name;
624         double value;
625     };
626
627     std::cout << "Loading parameters file...\n" << std::endl;
628     std::cout << "Please enter input file name: [Parameters.txt]";
629
630     std::string iname;
631     std::getline(std::cin, iname);
632
633     if (iname.empty()) {
634         iname = "Parameters.txt";
635     }
636
637     // the input stream
638     std::ifstream ist{ iname };
639
640     if (!ist)
641     {
642         std::cout << "\nCan't open input file " << iname << std::endl;
643         return false;
644     }
645
646     if (ist)
647     {
648         std::cout << "Reading the file " << iname << " ...\n" << std::endl;
649     }
650
651     // it will store the data
652     std::vector<Reading> parameters;
653
654     // reading from file
655     while (ist) {
656         std::string name{};
```

```cpp
657            double value{};
658            ist >> name >> value;
659            if (ist) {
660                parameters.push_back(Reading{ name, value });
661            }
662        }
663
664        // test the data
665        if (parameters.size() != 15)
666            return false;
667
668        // load in memory
669        for (auto parameter : parameters)
670        {
671            if (parameter.name == "GAS_MODE") gas_mode = parameter.value;
672
673            if (parameter.name == "NBALLS")    nballs = parameter.value;
674            if (parameter.name == "BALL_RADIUS") ball_radius = parameter.value;
675            if (parameter.name == "BALL_SPEED") ball_speed = parameter.value;
676            if (parameter.name == "BALL_MASS") ball_mass = parameter.value;
677            if (parameter.name == "BALL_GRAVITY") ball_gravity = parameter.value;
678
679            if (parameter.name == "IS_TESTING") is_testing = parameter.value;
680            if (parameter.name == "BALL0_SPEED") ball0_speed = parameter.value;
681            if (parameter.name == "BALL0_VEL_ANGLE") ball0_vel_angle = parameter.value;
682            if (parameter.name == "BALL1_SPEED") ball1_speed = parameter.value;
683            if (parameter.name == "BALL1_VEL_ANGLE") ball1_vel_angle = parameter.value;
684
685            if (parameter.name == "PISTON_MASS") piston_mass = parameter.value;
686            if (parameter.name == "PISTON_GRAVITY") piston_gravity = parameter.value;
687
688            if (parameter.name == "BOTTOM_TEMP_MIN") bottom_temp_min = parameter.value;
689            if (parameter.name == "BOTTOM_TEMP_MAX") bottom_temp_max = parameter.value;
690        }
691
692        return true;
693    }
694
695    void printParameters()
696    {
697        std::cout << "GAS_MODE " << gas_mode << std::endl;
698
699        std::cout << "NBALLS " << nballs << std::endl;
700        std::cout << "BALL_RADIUS " << ball_radius << std::endl;
701        std::cout << "BALL_SPEED " << ball_speed << std::endl;
702        std::cout << "BALL_MASS " << ball_mass << std::endl;
703        std::cout << "BALL_GRAVITY " << ball_gravity << std::endl;
704
705        std::cout << "IS_TESTING " << is_testing << std::endl;
706        std::cout << "BALL0_SPEED " << ball0_speed << std::endl;
707        std::cout << "BALL0_VEL_ANGLE " << ball0_vel_angle << std::endl;
708        std::cout << "BALL1_SPEED " << ball1_speed << std::endl;
709        std::cout << "BALL1_VEL_ANGLE " << ball1_vel_angle << std::endl;
710
711        std::cout << "PISTON_MASS " << piston_mass << std::endl;
```

```cpp
712        std::cout << "PISTON_GRAVITY " << piston_gravity << std::endl;
713
714        std::cout << "BOTTOM_TEMP_MIN " << bottom_temp_min << std::endl;
715        std::cout << "BOTTOM_TEMP_MAX " << bottom_temp_max << std::endl;
716 }
717
718
719 bool chooseSimulations()
720 {
721
722        std::cout << "Please, choose one example or read parameters from a file:" <<
723            std::endl;
724        std::cout << "[1] Three balls. (default)" << std::endl;
725        std::cout << "[2] One ball at rest. Piston with gravity." << std::endl;
726        std::cout << "[3] Eight balls at rest. Piston with gravity." << std::endl;
727        std::cout << "[4] Fifty balls (gas simulation approximation)." <<
728            " Piston with gravity." << std::endl;
729        std::cout << "[5] Load parameters from a file." << std::endl;
730
731        std::string input;
732        std::cout << "\nOption: ";
733        std::getline(std::cin, input);
734
735        int menuOption = 1;
736
737        if (!input.empty())
738        {
739            menuOption = stoi(input);
740        }
741
742        switch (menuOption)
743        {
744        case 1:
745            // Simulation mode
746            gas_mode = 0;
747            // Ball
748            nballs = 3;              // 100 max approx
749            ball_radius = 20;        // max 0.5 * WALL_WIDTH approx
750            ball_speed = 60;         // pixels/s (SPPED < RADIUS * 200 max approx)
751            ball_mass = 0.1;         // 0.01 * piston_mass min approx
752            ball_gravity = 0;        // if zero, simulate gas
753            // Piston
754            piston_mass = 10.0;
755            piston_gravity = 0.0;    // if zero, piston stops
756            break;
757
758        case 2:
759            // Simulation mode
760            gas_mode = 0;
761            // Ball
762            nballs = 1;              // 100 max approx
763            ball_radius = 20;        // max 0.5 * WALL_WIDTH approx
764            ball_speed = 0;          // pixels/s (SPPED < RADIUS * 200 max approx)
765            ball_mass = 0.2;         // 0.01 * piston_mass min approx
766            ball_gravity = 0;        // if zero, simulate gas
```

```
767          // Piston
768          piston_mass = 10.0;
769          piston_gravity = 10.0;    // if zero, piston stops
770          break;
771
772      case 3:
773          // Simulation mode
774          gas_mode = 0;
775          // Ball
776          nballs = 8;               // 100 max approx
777          ball_radius = 8;          // max 0.5 * WALL_WIDTH approx
778          ball_speed = 0;           // pixels/s (SPPED < RADIUS * 200 max approx)
779          ball_mass = 0.2;          // 0.01 * piston_mass min approx
780          ball_gravity = 0;         // if zero, simulate gas
781          // Piston
782          piston_mass = 10.0;
783          piston_gravity = 10.0;    // if zero, piston stops
784          break;
785
786      case 4:
787          // Simulation mode
788          gas_mode = 1;
789          // Ball
790          nballs = 50;              // 100 max approx
791          ball_radius = 4;          // max 0.5 * WALL_WIDTH approx
792          ball_speed = 60;          // pixels/s (SPPED < RADIUS * 200 max approx)
793          ball_mass = 0.1;          // 0.01 * piston_mass min approx
794          ball_gravity = 0;         // if zero, simulate gas
795          // Piston
796          piston_mass = 10.0;
797          piston_gravity = 10.0;    // if zero, piston stops
798          std::cout << "\nPlease, click on cylinder and increase energy" <<
799              " with '>' right key." << std::endl;
800          break;
801
802      case 5:
803          if (!loadParametersFromFile())
804          {
805              std::cout << "Can not load the parameters file." << std::endl;
806              std::cout << "Continue with the default? [y]" << std::endl;
807              std::string tc;
808              std::getline(std::cin, tc);
809              if (tc.empty()) {
810                  tc = "y";
811              }
812              if (tc == "y")
813              {
814                  // Simulation mode
815                  gas_mode = 0;
816                  // Ball
817                  nballs = 3;               // 100 max approx
818                  ball_radius = 20;         // max 0.5 * WALL_WIDTH approx
819                  ball_speed = 60;          // pixels/s (SPPED < RADIUS * 200 max approx)
820                  ball_mass = 0.1;          // 0.01 * piston_mass min approx
821                  ball_gravity = 0;         // if zero, simulate gas
```

```cpp
822                // Piston
823                piston_mass = 10.0;
824                piston_gravity = 0.0;  // if zero, piston stops
825                break;
826            }
827
828            return false;
829        }
830        break;
831
832    default:
833        // Simulation mode
834        gas_mode = 0;
835        // Ball
836        nballs = 3;               // 100 max approx.
837        ball_radius = 20;         // max 0.5 * WALL_WIDTH approx.
838        ball_speed = 60;          // pixels/s (SPPED < RADIUS * 200 max approx)
839        ball_mass = 0.1;          // 0.01 * piston_mass min approx
840        ball_gravity = 0;         // if zero, simulate gas
841        // Piston
842        piston_mass = 100.0;
843        piston_gravity = 0.0;     // if zero, piston stops
844        break;
845    }
846
847    std::cout << "\nPlease, verify the simulation parameters:\n" << std::endl;
848    printParameters();
849
850    std::cout << "\nPress enter to continue..." << std::endl;
851    std::cin.ignore();
852
853    return true;
854 }
855
```

```
 1  GAS_MODE   1
 2  NBALLS   80
 3  BALL_RADIUS   4
 4  BALL_SPEED   60
 5  BALL_MASS   0.2
 6  BALL_GRAVITY   0
 7  IS_TESTING   0
 8  BALL0_SPEED   50
 9  BALL0_VEL_ANGLE   0
10  BALL1_SPEED   50
11  BALL1_VEL_ANGLE   -180
12  PISTON_MASS   10.0
13  PISTON_GRAVITY   10.0
14  BOTTOM_TEMP_MIN   0.0
15  BOTTOM_TEMP_MAX   100.0
```

CMakeLists.txt

```
1   cmake_minimum_required (VERSION 3.5)
2
3   add_definitions(-std=c++17)
4
5   set(CXX_FLAGS, "-Wall")
6   set(CMAKE_CXX_FLAGS, "${CXX_FLAGS}")
7
8   project(MbcsProjectCmake)
9
10  set(CMAKE_MODULE_PATH ${CMAKE_MODULE_PATH} "${CMAKE_SOURCE_DIR}/cmake/")
11
12  find_package(SDL2 REQUIRED)
13  include_directories(${SDL2_INCLUDE_DIRS} src)
14
15  find_package(Threads)
16
17  add_executable(MbcsProjectCmake "src/Main.cpp" "src/CylinderObject.cpp"
18                  "src/Wall.cpp" "src/Ball.cpp")
19  string(STRIP "${SDL2_LIBRARIES}" SDL2_LIBRARIES)
20  target_link_libraries(MbcsProjectCmake ${CMAKE_THREAD_LIBS_INIT} ${SDL2_LIBRARIES} )
```

sdl2-config.cmake

```cmake
1   set(SDL2_INCLUDE_DIRS "${CMAKE_CURRENT_LIST_DIR}/include")
2
3   # Support both 32 and 64 bit builds
4   if (${CMAKE_SIZEOF_VOID_P} MATCHES 8)
5     set(SDL2_LIBRARIES "${CMAKE_CURRENT_LIST_DIR}/lib/x64/SDL2.lib"
6       "${CMAKE_CURRENT_LIST_DIR}/lib/x64/SDL2main.lib")
7   else ()
8     set(SDL2_LIBRARIES "${CMAKE_CURRENT_LIST_DIR}/lib/x86/SDL2.lib"
9       "${CMAKE_CURRENT_LIST_DIR}/lib/x86/SDL2main.lib")
10  endif ()
11
12  string(STRIP "${SDL2_LIBRARIES}" SDL2_LIBRARIES)
```

Appendix B

Here are the improvements in the program in Appendix A. There will not be the file "Constants.h" because all constants and global variables went to the file "Globals.h". There are two new files, "Piston.h" and "Piston.cpp", which are the separation of "processPiston" from the "Main.cpp".

Globals.h

```
1    #ifndef GLOBALS_H
2    #define GLOBALS_H
3
4    // Simulation mode
5    double gas_mode = 0;              // choose the mode of simulation
6                                      // "standard"(0) or "gas"(1)
7    // Ball
8    int nballs = 8;                   // 100 max approx
9    double ball_radius = 8;           // max 0.5 * WALL_WIDTH approx
10   double ball_speed = 0;            // pixels/s (SPPED < RADIUS * 200 max approx)
11   double ball_mass = 0.2;           // 0.01 * piston_mass min approx
12   double ball_gravity = 0;          // if zero, simulate gas
13   double ball_G = 0;                // gravitational constant
14   const double G_mult = 1e5;
15   int push_pull = 1;                // push-pull balls apart after collision
16   double coef_rest = 1.0;           // coef. restitution collision between balls
17
18   int is_testing = 0;               // choose the testing mode (1) or normal mode (0)
19   double ball0_speed = 10;          // in testing mode, first two balls
20   double ball0_vel_angle = 0;
21   double ball0_x = -1;
22   double ball0_y = -1;
23   double ball0_radius = -1;
24   double ball0_mass = -1;
25
26   double ball0_time = 0;            // will update the velocity after time
27   double ball0_delta_speed = 0;
28   double ball0_delta_angle = 0;
29
30   double ball1_speed = 10;
31   double ball1_vel_angle = -180;
32   double ball1_x = -1;
33   double ball1_y = -1;
34   double ball1_radius = -1;
35   double ball1_mass = -1;
36
37   // Piston
38   double piston_mass = 10.0;
```

```
39    double piston_gravity = 10.0;    // if zero, piston stops
40
41    // Bottom
42    double bottom_temp_min = 0.0;
43    double bottom_temp_max = 100.0;
44
45    // Background color (black:0 white:1)
46    int background_color = 1;
47
48    // Screen and wall width dimensions
49    double screen_width = 480;
50    double screen_height = 480;
51    double wall_width = 20;
52
53    // cylinder position and dimensions
54    double cylinder_center_position_x = screen_width / 2;
55    double cylinder_center_position_y = screen_height / 2;
56
57    double percent_width = 0.50;
58    double cylinder_width = screen_width * percent_width;
59
60    double percent_height = 0.80;
61    double cylinder_height = screen_height * percent_height;
62
63    double zoom_factor = 1.0;
64
65    #endif
```

```
1    #ifndef CylinderObject_H
2    #define CylinderObject_H
3
4    #include <vector>
5    #include <thread>
6    #include <mutex>
7
8
9    enum class ObjectType
10   {
11       noObject,
12       objectBall,
13       objectWall,
14   };
15
16   class CylinderObject
17   {
18   public:
19       // constructor / destructor
20       CylinderObject();
21       ~CylinderObject();
22
23       // getters / setters
24       int getID() { return _id; };
25       // position of object on canvas (Ball, Wall, or Piston)
26       void setPosition(double x, double y);
27       void getPosition(double& x, double& y);
28       // velocity of object
29       void setVelocity(double velX, double velY);
30       void getVelocity(double& velX, double& velY);
31       // speed of object
32       double getSpeed();
33       // mass of object
34       void setMass(double m);
35       double getMass();
36       ObjectType getType() { return _type; }
37
38       static std::mutex mtxCout;          // mutex shared by all cylinder objects for
39       // protecting cout
40
41       // typical behavior methods
42       virtual void simulate() {};         // This will be implemented by the Ball class
43
44   protected:
45       // member attributes
46       ObjectType    _type;                // identifies the class type
47       int _id;                            // every cylinder object has its own id
48       double    _posX, _posY;             // object position in pixels (center)
49       double _velX, _velY, _speed;        // velocity and speed in pixels/s
```

```cpp
50      double _mass;                       // object mass
51
52      std::vector<std::thread> _threads;  // holds all threads that have been launched
53                                          // within this object
54      std::mutex    _mutex;               // mutex to protect member attributes
55
56  private:
57      // member attributes
58      static int _idCnt;                  // global variable for counting ids
59
60  };
61
62
63  #endif
```

Ball.h

```cpp
1    #ifndef BALL_H
2    #define BALL_H
3
4    #include <mutex>
5    #include <deque>
6    #include <condition_variable>
7
8    #include "CylinderObject.h"
9    #include "Wall.h"
10
11
12   // forward declarations to avoid including cycle
13   class Wall;
14
15   // This is a message queue class for sending messages between threads
16   template <typename T>
17   class MessageQueue
18   {
19   public:
20       T receive();
21       void send(T&& msg);
22       int getSize();
23
24   private:
25       std::mutex _mutex;
26       std::condition_variable _cond;
27       std::deque<T> _queue;
28   };
29
30   enum class CollisionType {
31       wallCollision,
32       bottomCollision,
33       pistonCollision,
34   };
35
36   struct CollisionData {
37       CollisionType type;
38       double velY;
39   };
40
41   class Ball : public CylinderObject, public std::enable_shared_from_this<Ball>
42   {
43   public:
44       // constructor / destructor
45       Ball();
46
47       // getters / setters
48       void setWalls(std::vector<std::shared_ptr<Wall>> walls) { _walls = walls; }
49       void setBalls(std::vector<std::shared_ptr<Ball>> balls) { _balls = balls; }
```

```cpp
50
51        void setRadius(double r) { _radius = r; }
52        double getRadius() { return _radius; }
53
54        //This method will set a direction,calculating Vx and Vy based on speed and angle
55        void setSpecificDirection(double speed, double angle);
56
57        // This method will choose a random direction for the ball
58        void setRandomDirection(double speed);
59
60        // Gravitational Acceleration
61        void setGravity(double ball_gravity) { _ball_gravity = ball_gravity;  }
62        double getGravity() { return _ball_gravity; }
63
64        // Gravitational Constant (multiplied by a factor G_mult)
65        void setG(double ball_G) { _coef_G = ball_G; }
66        double getG() { return _coef_G; }
67
68        // Flag to set the "gas" mode model (piston counts the collisions)
69        void setGasMode(bool gas_mode) { _gas_mode = gas_mode;  }
70
71        // Coefficient of Restitution (for inelastic collisions)
72        void setCoefRestitution(double coef_e) { _coef_e = coef_e; }
73        double getCoefRestitution() { return _coef_e; }
74
75        // typical behaviour methods
76        bool dataIsAvailable();      // inform that there is a message from other thread
77        CollisionData receiveMsg();//receive msg from other thread (msg stored in queue)
78        void simulate();             // process ball movements
79        void setShutdown();          // set the flag to exit while-loop in simulate()
80
81        // miscellaneous
82        std::shared_ptr<Ball> get_shared_this() { return shared_from_this(); }
83        std::mutex ball_mutex;
84
85    private:
86        // typical behaviour methods
87        void play();
88        // check if has collided with a wall
89        bool checkWallCollision(double nextX, double nextY, std::shared_ptr<Wall> wall);
90        // check if has collided with another ball
91        bool checkBallCollision(double nextX, double nextY, std::shared_ptr<Ball> ball);
92        // receive direct message to shutdown (exit while-loop)
93        bool getShutdown();
94
95        // member attributes
96        double _radius;                  // ball radius
97        double _ball_gravity;            // gravity
98        double _coef_G;                  // gravitational constant
99        bool _gas_mode;                  // simulation mode
100       double _coef_e;                  // restitution coefficient
101       std::vector<std::shared_ptr<Wall>> _walls;//walls of cylinder on which ball is on
102       std::vector<std::shared_ptr<Ball>> _balls;//balls of cylinder on which ball is on
```

```
103     MessageQueue<CollisionData> _msgQueue;// msg queue for communications with main
104     bool _shutDown;                        // ask ball to end simulation
105   };
106
107   #endif
```

Piston.h

```
#ifndef PISTON_H
#define PISTON_H

#include "Ball.h"
#include "Wall.h"

// Prototype of the "processPiston", which will process the piston dynamics
void processPiston(std::shared_ptr<Wall> piston, std::shared_ptr<Wall> bottom,
    std::vector<std::shared_ptr<Ball>> balls, bool& finish);

#endif
```

```
1    #ifndef WALL_H
2    #define WALL_H
3
4    #include "CylinderObject.h"
5
6    enum class WallType
7    {
8        lateral,
9        piston,
10       cover,
11       bottom,
12   };
13
14   class Wall : public CylinderObject, public std::enable_shared_from_this<Wall>
15   {
16   public:
17       // constructor / destructor
18       Wall();
19
20       // getters / setters
21       // size (width and height)
22       void setSize(double w, double h);
23       void getSize(double& w, double& h);
24
25       // heat or temperature
26       void setHeat(double ht);
27       double getHeat();
28
29       // type of the wall: lateral, piston, bottom
30       void setWallType(WallType type) { _wallType = type; }
31       WallType getWallType() { return _wallType; }
32
33       // miscellaneous
34       std::shared_ptr<Wall> get_shared_this() { return shared_from_this(); }
35
36       std::mutex wall_mutex;        // wall mutex
37
38   private:
39
40       // member attributes
41       double _width, _height;       // object width and height in pixels
42       double _temp;                 // wall temperature
43       WallType _wallType;           // wall type
44
45   };
46
47
48   #endif
```

```
1    #include <algorithm>
2
3    #include "CylinderObject.h"
4
5
6    // init static variables
7    int CylinderObject::_idCnt = 0;
8    std::mutex CylinderObject::mtxCout;
9
10   CylinderObject::CylinderObject()
11   {
12       _type = ObjectType::noObject;
13       _id = _idCnt;
14       _posX = 0;
15       _posY = 0;
16       _velX = 0;
17       _velY = 0;
18       _speed = 0;
19       _mass = 0;
20       _idCnt++;
21   }
22
23   void CylinderObject::setPosition(double x, double y)
24   {
25       std::lock_guard<std::mutex> lock(_mutex);
26       _posX = x;
27       _posY = y;
28   }
29
30   void  CylinderObject::getPosition(double& x, double& y)
31   {
32       std::lock_guard<std::mutex> lock(_mutex);
33       x = _posX;
34       y = _posY;
35   }
36
37   void CylinderObject::setVelocity(double velX, double velY)
38   {
39       std::lock_guard<std::mutex> lock(_mutex);
40       _velX = velX;
41       _velY = velY;
42       _speed = sqrt(pow(velX, 2) + pow(velY, 2));
43   }
44
45   void CylinderObject::getVelocity(double& velX, double& velY)
46   {
47       std::lock_guard<std::mutex> lock(_mutex);
48       velX = _velX;
49       velY = _velY;
```

```cpp
50     }
51
52     double CylinderObject::getSpeed()
53     {
54         std::lock_guard<std::mutex> lock(_mutex);
55         _speed = sqrt(pow(_velX, 2) + pow(_velY, 2));
56         return _speed;
57     }
58
59     void CylinderObject::setMass(double mass)
60     {
61         _mass = mass;
62     }
63
64     double CylinderObject::getMass()
65     {
66         return _mass;
67     }
68
69     CylinderObject::~CylinderObject()
70     {
71         // set up thread barrier before this object is destroyed
72         std::for_each(_threads.begin(), _threads.end(), [](std::thread& t) {
73             t.join();
74         });
75     }
```

```cpp
1    #include <iostream>
2    #include <thread>
3    #include <future>
4    #include <memory>
5    #include <random>
6    #include <algorithm>
7    #include <cmath>
8    #include <array>
9    #include <iomanip>
10   #include <string>
11
12   #include "Ball.h"
13
14   // Variables defined at Globals.h
15   extern double cylinder_center_position_x;
16   extern double cylinder_width;
17   extern double cylinder_center_position_y;
18   extern double cylinder_height;
19   extern int push_pull;
20   extern int is_testing;
21   extern double ball0_time;
22   extern double ball0_delta_speed;
23   extern double ball0_delta_angle;
24
25
26   template <typename T>
27   T MessageQueue<T>::receive()
28   {
29
30       std::unique_lock<std::mutex> uLock(_mutex); // needs unique_lock because the lock
31       // will be temporarily unlocked inside wait
32       _cond.wait(uLock, [this] { return !_queue.empty(); });   // enter the wait state,
33       // release the lock and resume if new data is available
34
35       T msg = std::move(_queue.back());
36       _queue.pop_back();
37
38       //std::cout << "Message " << msg  << " has been received from the Ball msg queue"
39       // << std::endl;
40
41       return msg;
42   }
43
44   template <typename T>
45   void MessageQueue<T>::send(T&& msg)
46   {
47
48       std::lock_guard<std::mutex> uLock(_mutex);
49
```

```
50      //std::cout << "Message " <<  msg << " has been sent to the Ball msg queue"
51      // << std::endl;
52
53      _queue.push_back(std::move(msg));
54      _cond.notify_one();
55
56  }
57
58  template <typename T>
59  int MessageQueue<T>::getSize()
60  {
61      std::lock_guard<std::mutex> uLock(_mutex);
62      return _queue.size();
63  }
64
65  // helper function declaration
66  double distanceToPoint(double x1, double y1, double x2, double y2);
67  bool squareCircleCollision(double x1, double y1, double w1, double h1,
68                             double x2, double y2, double r2);
69  bool circleCircleCollision(double x1, double y1, double r1,
70                             double x2, double y2, double r2);
71  void resolveCollision(double& posX, double& posY, double& velX, double& velY,
72                        double speed, double mass, double radius,
73                        double& otherX, double& otherY,
74                        double& otherVx, double& otherVy,
75                        double otherSpeed, double otherM, double otherR, bool isWall,
76                        double coef_e, double coef_G);
77
78  Ball::Ball()
79  {
80      _type = ObjectType::objectBall;
81      _radius = 0;
82      _velX = 0;
83      _velY = 0;
84      _speed = 0;
85      _shutDown = false;
86      _ball_gravity = 0;
87      _gas_mode = false;
88      _coef_e = 0;
89      _coef_G = 0;
90  }
91
92
93  void Ball::setSpecificDirection(double speed, double angle)
94  {
95      // set velocity
96      double vx, vy;
97      double pi = acos(-1);
98      vx = speed * cos(angle * 2 * pi / 360);
99      vy = -speed * sin(angle * 2 * pi / 360);
100     setVelocity(vx, vy);
101 }
102
```

```cpp
103    void Ball::setRandomDirection(double speed)
104    {
105        // pick angle at random and set direction of the ball
106        double angle;
107        std::random_device rd;
108        std::mt19937 generator(rd());
109        std::array<double, 5> intervals{ -60.0, 60.0, 120.0, 240.0, 360.0 };
110        std::array<double, 4> weights{ 1.0, 1.0, 1.0, 1.0 };
111        std::piecewise_constant_distribution<double>
112            distribution(intervals.begin(), intervals.end(), weights.begin());
113        angle = distribution(generator);
114
115        std::cout << "Angle " << angle << std::endl;
116
117        // set velocity
118        setSpecificDirection(speed, angle);
119    }
120
121    bool Ball::dataIsAvailable()
122    {
123        return (_msgQueue.getSize() > 0);
124    }
125
126    CollisionData Ball::receiveMsg()
127    {
128        return _msgQueue.receive();
129    }
130
131    bool Ball::getShutdown()
132    {
133        return _shutDown;
134    }
135
136    void Ball::setShutdown()
137    {
138        _shutDown = true;
139    }
140
141    // implement the virtual function that will execute a member function into a thread
142    void Ball::simulate()
143    {
144        // Start a thread with the member function "play" and the object "this"
145        // Add the created thread into the _threads vector of parent class (using
146        // emplace_back which means move semantics)
147        _threads.emplace_back(std::thread(&Ball::play, this));
148    }
149
150    // function which is executed in athread
151    void Ball::play()
152    {
153
154        // print Ball id and thread id
155        std::unique_lock<std::mutex> uLock(mtxCout);
```

```cpp
156    std::cout << "Ball::simulate Ball _id=" << getID() << "  thread id=" <<
157    std::this_thread::get_id() << std::endl;
158    uLock.unlock();
159
160    long count = 0;
161
162    // initialize variables
163
164    // define cycle duration (to update ball position and check cylinder)
165    int cycleDuration = 10;   // duration of a single simulation cycle in ms
166
167    // init stop watch
168    std::chrono::time_point<std::chrono::system_clock> lastUpdate, simBegin;
169    lastUpdate = std::chrono::system_clock::now();
170    simBegin = std::chrono::system_clock::now();
171
172    // infinite simulation loop
173    while (!getShutdown())
174    {
175        // compute time difference to stop watch (in ms)
176        auto timeSinceLastUpdate = std::chrono::duration_cast<std::chrono
177            ::milliseconds>(std::chrono::system_clock::now() -
178                lastUpdate).count();
179
180        // if past cycle time, update position and check cylinder
181        if (timeSinceLastUpdate >= cycleDuration)
182        {
183
184            // reset stop watch for next cycle
185            lastUpdate = std::chrono::system_clock::now();
186
187            // calc next position
188            double velX, velY, nextX, nextY;
189            double posX, posY, dx, dy;
190            getVelocity(velX, velY);
191            getPosition(posX, posY);
192
193            dx = velX * (timeSinceLastUpdate / 1000.0); // dx = Vx * dt
194
195            // calc gravity acceleration effect
196            dy = velY * (timeSinceLastUpdate / 1000.0) +
197                0.5 * _ball_gravity * pow(timeSinceLastUpdate / 1000.0, 2.0);
198
199            double dVy = _ball_gravity * (timeSinceLastUpdate / 1000.0);   //dVy=Ay*dt
200
201
202            // calc gravitational/force field
203            // F = G * m1 * m2 / r^2
204            // Gf = G * m2 / r^2
205            int thisBallId = getID();
206
207            double Gf = 0.0;     // field
208            double Gfx = 0.0;
```

```cpp
209            double Gfy = 0.0;
210            double coef_G = getG();
211            double dGVx = 0.0;
212            double dGVy = 0.0;
213
214            if (coef_G > 0 || coef_G < 0)
215            {
216                for (auto ball : _balls)
217                {
218                    int otherBallId = ball->getID();
219                    if (thisBallId != otherBallId)
220                    {
221                        double otherX, otherY;
222                        ball->getPosition(otherX, otherY);
223
224                        double m2 = ball->getMass();
225                        double r = distanceToPoint(posX + dx/2, posY + dy/2,
226                            otherX, otherY);
227                        Gf = coef_G * m2 / (r * r);
228                        double angle = atan2(otherY -posY -dy/2, otherX -posX -dx/2);
229                        Gfx += Gf * cos(angle);
230                        Gfy += Gf * sin(angle);
231                    }
232                }
233
234                // calc gravitational acceleration effect
235                dx += 0.5 * Gfx * pow(timeSinceLastUpdate / 1000.0, 2.0);
236                dy += 0.5 * Gfy * pow(timeSinceLastUpdate / 1000.0, 2.0);
237
238                dGVx = Gfx * (timeSinceLastUpdate / 1000.0);   // dV = A*dt
239                dGVy = Gfy * (timeSinceLastUpdate / 1000.0);
240            }
241
242            // update velocity before entering the collision
243            velX += dGVx;
244            velY += dVy + dGVy;
245
246            // update delta_speed in ball0
247            if ( _id == _balls.at(0)->getID() &&
248                (std::chrono::duration_cast<std::chrono::milliseconds>
249                (std::chrono::system_clock::now() - simBegin).count() > ball0_time)&&
250                ball0_time != 0 && is_testing == 1) {
251                velX += ball0_delta_speed * cos(ball0_delta_angle * acos(-1) / 180);
252                velY += ball0_delta_speed * (-1.0) * sin(ball0_delta_angle *
253                    acos(-1) / 180);
254                ball0_time = 0;
255            }
256
257            setVelocity(velX, velY);
258
259            // print time to orbit
260            if (_id == _balls.at(0)->getID() &&
261                ball0_time != 0 && getSpeed() < 1.0 && is_testing == 1) {
```

```
262        auto time = std::chrono::duration_cast<std::chrono::milliseconds>
263            (std::chrono::system_clock::now() - simBegin).count();
264        double x1, y1, x2, y2;
265        _balls.at(0)->getPosition(x1, y1);
266        _balls.at(1)->getPosition(x2, y2);
267        double orbit = distanceToPoint(x1, y1, x2, y2);
268        uLock.lock();
269        std::cout << "speed: " << getSpeed() << " time: " << time <<
270            " orbit:" << std::setprecision(6) << orbit << std::endl;
271        uLock.unlock();
272    }
273
274    // next position
275    nextX = posX + dx;
276    nextY = posY + dy;
277
278    // check if the ball has collided
279    bool hasCollided = false;
280
281    // process ball with wall collision
282    // m0*v0i + m1*v1i = m0*v0f + m1*v1f
283    // Ec0i + Ec1i >= Ec0f + Ec1f
284    for (auto wall : _walls) {
285
286        // process piston->ball collision (the piston moves in y axis):
287        if (wall->getWallType() == WallType::piston)
288        {
289            // begin of piston critical section
290            std::unique_lock<std::mutex> pLock(wall->wall_mutex);
291
292            // if ball is inside the piston: flag the collision
293            if (checkWallCollision(nextX, nextY, wall)) {
294
295                hasCollided = true;
296
297                double otherVx, otherVy;
298                wall->getVelocity(otherVx, otherVy);
299                double x, y, w, h;
300                wall->getPosition(x, y);
301                wall->getSize(w, h);
302
303                double velCollisionGas = velY;
304
305                double otherX, otherY;
306                otherX = posX;//like collision with a ball at the same x coordinate
307                otherY = y;
308
309                double speed = getSpeed();
310                double otherSpeed = wall->getSpeed();
311
312                double mass = _mass;
313                double otherM = wall->getMass();
314
```

```
315              // limit pistom movement to the cylinder
316              if (otherY <= (cylinder_center_position_y -
317                  cylinder_height * 0.5) * 1.001)
318              {
319                  otherM = 1e100;
320
321              }
322
323              double radius = _radius;
324              double otherR = h / 2;   // it is like a collision with a ball
325              // at the same x coordinate, with r = h/2
326
327              double coef_e = getCoefRestitution();
328
329              resolveCollision(posX, posY, velX, velY,
330                                speed, mass, radius,
331                                otherX, otherY, otherVx, otherVy,
332                                otherSpeed, otherM, otherR, false,
333                                coef_e, coef_G);
334
335              // Two models of simulation: in the gas mode, the piston is
336              // processed in main
337              if (!(_gas_mode))
338              {
339                  // update positions and velocities
340                  wall->setVelocity(0, otherVy);
341                  wall->setPosition(x, otherY);
342
343                  setVelocity(velX, velY);
344                  setPosition(posX, posY);
345
346              }
347              else
348              {
349                  // update ball position and velocity
350                  setVelocity(velX, velY);
351                  setPosition(posX, posY);
352
353                  // msg to main, to update piston:
354                  _msgQueue.send({ CollisionType::pistonCollision,
355                                    velCollisionGas - velY });
356              }
357
358          }
359
360      // end of piston critical section
361      pLock.unlock();
362
363      if (hasCollided) {
364          break;
365      }
366
367  }
```

```
368
369             // process collision with laterals
370             if (wall->getWallType() == WallType::lateral)
371             {
372
373                 // if there is a collision, change ball direction
374                 if (checkWallCollision(nextX, nextY, wall)) {
375
376                     //std::cout << "ball with lateral collision" << std::endl;
377
378                     hasCollided = true;
379
380                     double otherVx, otherVy;   // wall
381                     otherVx = 0;
382                     otherVy = 0;
383                     double x, y, w, h;
384                     wall->getPosition(x, y);
385                     wall->getSize(w, h);
386
387                     double coef_e = getCoefRestitution();
388
389                     double otherX, otherY;
390                     otherX = x;   // like collision with a ball at the same x coordinate
391                     otherY = posY;
392
393                     double speed = getSpeed();
394                     double otherSpeed = 0;
395
396                     double mass = _mass;
397                     double otherM = 1e100;
398
399                     double radius = _radius;
400                     double otherR = w / 2;   // it is like a collision with a ball
401                     // at the same y coordinate, with r = w/2
402
403                     resolveCollision(posX, posY, velX, velY,
404                                      speed, mass, radius,
405                                      otherX, otherY, otherVx, otherVy,
406                                      otherSpeed, otherM, otherR, true,
407                                      coef_e, coef_G);
408
409                     // update velocity
410                     setVelocity(velX, velY);
411
412                     // update position
413                     setPosition(posX, posY);
414
415                     break;
416
417                 }
418
419             }
420
```

```cpp
421                    // process collision with bottom
422                    if (wall->getWallType() == WallType::bottom)
423                    {
424
425                        if (checkWallCollision(nextX, nextY, wall)) {
426
427                            //std::cout << "ball with bottom collision" << std::endl;
428
429                            hasCollided = true;
430
431                            double otherVx, otherVy;   // bottom
432                            otherVx = 0;
433                            otherVy = 0;
434                            double x, y, w, h;
435                            wall->getPosition(x, y);
436                            wall->getSize(w, h);
437
438                            double coef_e = getCoefRestitution();
439
440                            double otherX, otherY;
441                            otherX = posX; //like collision with a ball at the same x coordinate
442                            otherY = y;
443
444                            double speed = getSpeed();
445                            double otherSpeed = 0;
446
447                            double mass = _mass;
448                            double otherM = 1e100;
449
450                            double radius = _radius;
451                            double otherR = h / 2;   // it is like a collision with a ball
452                            // at the same x coordinate, with r = h/2
453
454                            resolveCollision(posX, posY, velX, velY,
455                                             speed, mass, radius,
456                                             otherX, otherY, otherVx, otherVy,
457                                             otherSpeed, otherM, otherR, true,
458                                             coef_e, coef_G);
459
460                            // Adjust ball velocity to aprox temperature effect of bottom
461                            if (wall->getWallType() == WallType::bottom) {
462                                if (abs(velY) < 1.0 * wall->getHeat())
463                                {
464                                    velY = -1.0 * wall->getHeat();
465                                }
466                            }
467
468                            // update velocity
469                            setVelocity(velX, velY);
470                            // update position
471                            setPosition(posX, posY);
472
473                            break;
```

```
474
475                     }
476
477                 }
478
479             } // eof ball-wall collision
480
481
482             // process ball with ball collisions
483             // m0*v0i + m1*v1i = m0*v0f + m1*v1f
484             // Ec0i + Ec1i >= Ec0f + Ec1f
485             if (!hasCollided)
486             {
487                 int thisBallId = getID();
488                 for (auto ball : _balls)
489                 {
490
491                     int otherBallId = ball->getID();
492
493                     if (thisBallId != otherBallId &&
494                         checkBallCollision(nextX, nextY, ball))
495                     {
496                         //uLock.lock();
497                         //std::cout << "ball:" << thisBallId << " with ball:" <<
498                         //    otherBallId <<  " collision" << std::endl;
499                         //uLock.unlock();
500
501                         // if there is a collision, change ball direction
502                         // elastic collision
503
504                         hasCollided = true;
505
506                         double otherX, otherY;
507                         ball->getPosition(otherX, otherY);
508
509                         double otherVx, otherVy;
510                         ball->getVelocity(otherVx, otherVy);
511
512                         // approx. do not use all dGV (collide first)
513                         velX = velX - 0.5 * dGVx;
514                         velY = velY - 0.5 * dGVy;
515
516                         double speed = sqrt(pow(velX, 2.0) + pow(velY, 2.0));
517                         double otherSpeed = ball->getSpeed();
518
519                         double mass = getMass();
520                         double otherM = ball->getMass();
521
522                         double radius = getRadius();
523                         double otherR = ball->getRadius();
524
525                         double coef_e = getCoefRestitution();
526
```

```
527
528                            resolveCollision(posX, posY, velX, velY,
529                                             speed, mass, radius,
530                                             otherX, otherY, otherVx, otherVy,
531                                             otherSpeed, otherM, otherR, false,
532                                             coef_e, coef_G);
533
534                       // update velocities
535                       setVelocity(velX, velY);
536                       ball->setVelocity(otherVx, otherVy);
537
538                       // update positions
539                       setPosition(posX, posY);
540                       ball->setPosition(otherX, otherY);
541
542                   }
543
544               }
545
546           } // eof new ball-ball collision
547
548
549           // if has not colided, just update position (velocity has been updated)
550           if (!hasCollided) {
551               setPosition(nextX, nextY);
552           }
553
554       } // eof cycle
555
556
557       // sleep at every iteration to reduce CPU usage
558       std::this_thread::sleep_for(std::chrono::milliseconds(1));
559
560   } // eof simulation loop
561
562
563   // print Ball id and thread id
564   uLock.lock();
565   std::cout << "Ball::simulate closing Ball _id=" << getID() << "  thread id=" <<
566       std::this_thread::get_id() << std::endl;
567   uLock.unlock();
568 }
569
570 // Verify and process the collision of the ball with the cylinder walls
571 bool Ball::checkWallCollision(double nextX, double nextY, std::shared_ptr<Wall> wall)
572 {
573     double x, y, w, h;
574     bool collision = false;
575
576     wall->getPosition(x, y);
577     wall->getSize(w, h);
578     collision = squareCircleCollision(x, y, w, h, nextX, nextY, _radius);
579
```

```
580        return collision;
581    }
582
583    // Verify and process the collision of the ball with the cylinder walls
584    bool Ball::checkBallCollision(double nextX, double nextY, std::shared_ptr<Ball> ball)
585    {
586        double x, y, r;
587        bool collision = false;
588
589        ball->getPosition(x, y);
590        r = ball->getRadius();
591        collision = circleCircleCollision(nextX, nextY, _radius, x, y, r);
592
593        return collision;
594    }
595
596    // verify collision between square x1,y1,w1,h1 and circle x2,y2,r2
597    bool squareCircleCollision(double x1, double y1, double w1, double h1,
598                               double x2, double y2, double r2)
599    {
600        double closestX, closestY;
601        bool collision = false;
602
603        // find the closest x coordinate of the wall to the circle
604        if (x1 + w1 * 0.5 < x2 - r2) { closestX = x1 + w1 * 0.5; }
605        else if (x1 - w1 * 0.5 > x2 + r2) { closestX = x1 - w1 * 0.5; }
606        else { closestX = x2; }
607
608        // find the closest y coordinate of the wall to the circle
609        if (y1 + h1 * 0.5 < y2 - r2) { closestY = y1 + h1 * 0.5; }
610        else if (y1 - h1 * 0.5 > y2 + r2) { closestY = y1 - h1 * 0.5; }
611        else { closestY = y2; }
612
613        if (distanceToPoint(x2, y2, closestX, closestY) < (r2 - 1e-3)) {
614            collision = true;
615        }
616
617        return collision;
618    }
619
620    // verify collision between circle x1,y1,r1 and circle x2,y2,r2
621    bool circleCircleCollision(double x1, double y1, double r1,
622                               double x2, double y2, double r2)
623    {
624        double distance;
625        bool collision;
626
627        distance = distanceToPoint(x1, y1, x2, y2);
628        collision = (distance < (r1 + r2 - 1e-3));
629
630        return collision;
631    }
632
```

```
633    double distanceToPoint(double x1, double y1, double x2, double y2)
634    {
635        double distance;
636
637        distance = sqrt(pow(x1 - x2, 2.0) + pow(y1 - y2, 2.0));
638
639        return distance;
640    }
641
642    // resolve collision elastic
643    void resolveCollision(double& posX, double& posY, double& velX, double& velY,
644                          double speed, double mass, double radius,
645                          double& otherX, double& otherY,double& otherVx,double& otherVy,
646                          double otherSpeed, double otherM, double otherR, bool isWall,
647                          double coef_e, double coef_G)
648    {
649
650        if (mass == 0 || otherM == 0)
651        {
652            std::cout << "Error: mass is zero!" << std::endl;
653            return;
654        }
655
656        double angleCol = atan2(otherY - posY, otherX - posX);
657        double direction = atan2(velY, velX);
658        double otherDirection = atan2(otherVy, otherVx);
659
660        double new_xspeed = speed * cos(direction - angleCol);
661        double new_yspeed = speed * sin(direction - angleCol);
662
663        double new_xspeedOther = otherSpeed * cos(otherDirection - angleCol);
664        double new_yspeedOther = otherSpeed * sin(otherDirection - angleCol);
665
666        double final_xspeed = ((mass - coef_e * otherM) * new_xspeed +
667            (otherM + coef_e * otherM) * new_xspeedOther) / (mass + otherM);
668        double final_xspeedOther = ((mass + coef_e * mass) * new_xspeed +
669            (otherM - coef_e * mass) * new_xspeedOther) / (mass + otherM);
670        double final_yspeed = new_yspeed;
671        double final_yspeedOther = new_yspeedOther;
672
673        double cosAngle = cos(angleCol);
674        double sinAngle = sin(angleCol);
675
676        double newVelX, newVelY;
677        newVelX = cosAngle * final_xspeed - sinAngle * final_yspeed;
678        newVelY = sinAngle * final_xspeed + cosAngle * final_yspeed;
679
680        double newOtherVelX, newOtherVelY;
681        newOtherVelX = cosAngle * final_xspeedOther - sinAngle * final_yspeedOther;
682        newOtherVelY = sinAngle * final_xspeedOther + cosAngle * final_yspeedOther;
683
684        // get the minimum translation distance to push balls apart after intersecting
685        struct Position {
```

```
686        double x;
687        double y;
688        double length() {
689            return sqrt(pow(x, 2.0) + pow(y, 2.0));
690        }
691    } pos1, pos2, posDiff, mtd;
692
693    pos1.x = posX;
694    pos1.y = posY;
695    pos2.x = otherX;
696    pos2.y = otherY;
697    posDiff.x = pos1.x - pos2.x;
698    posDiff.y = pos1.y - pos2.y;
699
700    double d = posDiff.length();
701    double k = (((radius + otherR) - d) / d);
702    mtd.x = posDiff.x * k;
703    mtd.y = posDiff.y * k;
704
705    double im = 1 / mass;
706    double imOther = 1 / otherM;
707
708    // push-pull them apart based off their mass, if the flag was set
709    if (push_pull == 1 ) {
710        pos1.x = pos1.x + mtd.x * (im / (im + imOther));
711        pos1.y = pos1.y + mtd.y * (im / (im + imOther));
712        pos2.x = pos2.x - mtd.x * (imOther / (im + imOther));
713        pos2.y = pos2.y - mtd.y * (imOther / (im + imOther));
714
715
716        // Process ball with wall collision generated by the pushing balls apart
717        if ((pos1.x + radius >= cylinder_center_position_x + cylinder_width / 2) ||
718            (pos1.x - radius <= cylinder_center_position_x - cylinder_width / 2))
719        {
720            newVelX = -1.0 * newVelX;
721        }
722
723        if ((pos1.y + radius >= cylinder_center_position_y + cylinder_height / 2) ||
724            (pos1.y - radius <= cylinder_center_position_y - cylinder_height / 2))
725        {
726            newVelY = -1.0 * newVelY;
727        }
728
729
730        // if other is a wall of the cylinder, do not process (is not valid)
731        if (((pos2.x + otherR >= cylinder_center_position_x + cylinder_width / 2) ||
732            (pos2.x - otherR <= cylinder_center_position_x - cylinder_width / 2)) &&
733            !isWall)
734        {
735            newOtherVelX = -1.0 * newOtherVelX;
736        }
737
738
```

```
739          // if other is a wall of the cylinder, do not process (is not valid)
740          if (((pos2.y + otherR >= cylinder_center_position_y + cylinder_height / 2) ||
741              (pos2.y - otherR <= cylinder_center_position_y - cylinder_height / 2)) &&
742              !isWall)
743          {
744              newOtherVelY = -1.0 * newOtherVelY;
745
746          }
747
748
749      }
750
751      velX = newVelX;
752      velY = newVelY;
753
754      posX = pos1.x;
755      posY = pos1.y;
756
757      otherVx = newOtherVelX;
758      otherVy = newOtherVelY;
759
760      otherX = pos2.x;
761      otherY = pos2.y;
762
763  }
764
765
```

```cpp
1   #include "Wall.h"
2
3   Wall::Wall()
4   {
5       _type = ObjectType::objectWall;
6       _wallType = WallType::lateral;
7       _width = 0;
8       _height = 0;
9       _temp = 0;
10  }
11
12  void  Wall::setSize(double w, double h)
13  {
14      _width = w;
15      _height = h;
16  }
17
18  void  Wall::getSize(double& w, double& h)
19  {
20      w = _width;
21      h = _height;
22  }
23
24  void Wall::setHeat(double ht)
25  {
26      std::lock_guard<std::mutex> lock(_mutex);
27      _temp = ht;
28  }
29
30  double Wall::getHeat()
31  {
32      std::lock_guard<std::mutex> lock(_mutex);
33      return _temp;
34  }
```

```cpp
1    #include <iostream>
2    #include <iomanip>
3
4    #include "Ball.h"
5    #include "Wall.h"
6
7    // Variables defined at Globals.h
8    extern double gas_mode;
9    extern double cylinder_center_position_x;
10   extern double cylinder_width;
11   extern double cylinder_center_position_y;
12   extern double cylinder_height;
13   extern double wall_width;
14   extern double piston_mass;
15   extern double piston_gravity;
16   extern double coef_rest;
17   extern int is_testing;
18   extern double ball0_time;
19   extern double ball0_delta_speed;
20
21
22   void processPiston(std::shared_ptr<Wall> piston, std::shared_ptr<Wall> bottom,
23       std::vector<std::shared_ptr<Ball>> balls, bool& finish)
24   {
25
26       // Set to piston dynamics
27       long pistoncollisions = 0;
28       double upForce = 0.0;
29       double mv = 0.0;
30       double avgUpForce = 0.0;
31       double downForce = 0.0;    // for testing
32       downForce = piston_gravity * piston_mass;
33       double pistonVel = 0.0;
34       int cycleDuration = 10;  // define cycle duration (ms) to calc up force
35       bool gasMode = (gas_mode > 0);
36       double temp = 0;
37
38
39       // init stop watch
40       std::chrono::time_point<std::chrono::system_clock> lastUpdate;
41       lastUpdate = std::chrono::system_clock::now();
42
43       auto f0 = [balls, bottom, cycleDuration, gasMode, &avgUpForce, &downForce,
44           &temp, &finish]()
45       {
46           long simTime = 0;
47           while (!finish) {
48               std::this_thread::sleep_for(std::chrono::milliseconds(1000));
49               // count balls inside piston (testing)
```

```
50              int count = 0;
51              for (auto ball : balls)
52              {
53                  double x, y;
54                  ball->getPosition(x, y);
55                  if (x > cylinder_center_position_x - cylinder_width * 0.5 && x <
56                      cylinder_center_position_x + cylinder_width * 0.5 &&
57                      y > cylinder_center_position_y - cylinder_height * 0.5 && y <
58                      cylinder_center_position_y + cylinder_height * 0.5)
59                  {
60                      count++;
61                  }
62                  else {
63                      ball->setShutdown();
64                  }
65              }
66
67              std::unique_lock<std::mutex> uLock(bottom->mtxCout);
68              std::cout << "Time:" << simTime << "\t";
69              std::cout << "balls:" << count << "    ";
70
71              if (gasMode) {
72                  std::cout << "gas avg(1.0s) up force : " << std::fixed <<
73                      std::setprecision(2) << abs(avgUpForce) << "  \t";
74                  std::cout << "piston down force: " << std::setprecision(2) <<
75                      downForce << " \t";
76              }
77
78              temp = bottom->getHeat();
79              std::cout << "~temp(bottom) : " << std::setprecision(2) << temp <<
80                  std::endl;
81
82               //   print orbit distance
83              if (ball0_delta_speed != 0 && is_testing == 1 && ball0_time == 0) {
84                  double x1, y1, x2, y2;
85                  balls.at(0)->getPosition(x1, y1);
86                  balls.at(1)->getPosition(x2, y2);
87                  double orbit = sqrt(pow(x1 - x2, 2.0) + pow(y1 - y2, 2.0));
88                  std::cout << "speed: " << std::setprecision(6) <<
89                      balls.at(0)->getSpeed() << "   >>> orbit:" << orbit <<
90                      " <<<\n" << std::endl;
91              }
92
93              uLock.unlock();
94
95              simTime++;
96          }
97      };
98
99      std::thread t1(f0);          // thread for monitoring and testing
100
101
102      while (!finish)
```

```cpp
103      {
104
105          // compute time difference (in ms)
106          auto timeSinceLastUpdate =
107              std::chrono::duration_cast<std::chrono::milliseconds>
108              (std::chrono::system_clock::now() - lastUpdate).count();
109
110          // Receive and process msg from balls about a collision with the piston
111          for (auto ball : balls)
112          {
113              while (ball->dataIsAvailable())
114              {
115                  //std::cout << "Main: ball msg available" << std::endl;
116                  CollisionData msg = ball->receiveMsg();
117                  CollisionType colType = msg.type;
118                  double velocity = msg.velY;      // downward is positve
119                  switch (colType) {
120                  case CollisionType::bottomCollision:
121                      //std::cout << "ball-bottom collision" << std::endl;
122                      break;
123                  case CollisionType::pistonCollision:
124                      //std::cout << "*gas* ball-piston collision " << "mv: "
125                      //<< mv << std::endl;
126                      pistoncollisions++;
127                      mv += ball->getMass() * velocity;     // change in momentum
128                      break;
129                  }
130              }
131
132          }
133
134
135          // Process piston dymamics
136          if (timeSinceLastUpdate > cycleDuration) {
137
138              // begin of critical section
139              std::unique_lock<std::mutex> pLock(piston->wall_mutex);
140
141              // F * t = m * v
142              upForce = mv / (timeSinceLastUpdate / 1000.0);
143              avgUpForce = avgUpForce + upForce / (1000.0 / cycleDuration)- avgUpForce/
144                  (1000.0 / cycleDuration);    // 1000ms average (for printing)
145
146              double posX, posY;
147              double velX, velY;
148              double acceleration;
149
150              piston->getPosition(posX, posY);
151              piston->getVelocity(velX, velY);
152
153              // F = m * a
154              Acceleration =(upForce + downForce)/(piston_mass + 1e-10);   // downward =
155              // positive; prevent overflow
```

156

```cpp
156
157            // calc piston position  (x - x0) = vo * t + 1/2 * a * t^2
158            posY = posY + velY * (timeSinceLastUpdate / 1000.0) +
159                0.5 * acceleration * pow(timeSinceLastUpdate / 1000.0, 2.0);//approx.
160
161            // piston velocity for next cycle
162            pistonVel = velY + acceleration * (timeSinceLastUpdate / 1000.0);
163
164            // piston at the top: no velocity upward
165            if (posY < (cylinder_center_position_y - cylinder_height * 0.5))
166            {
167                if (pistonVel < 0) pistonVel = -coef_rest * pistonVel;
168                posY = cylinder_center_position_y - cylinder_height * 0.5;
169            }
170            // piston at the bottom: no velocity downward
171            else if (posY > (cylinder_center_position_y +
172                cylinder_height * 0.5 - wall_width))
173            {
174                if (pistonVel > 0) pistonVel = -coef_rest * pistonVel;
175                posY = cylinder_center_position_y +
176                    cylinder_height * 0.5 - wall_width;
177            }
178
179            // update piston
180            piston->setPosition(posX, posY);
181            piston->setVelocity(0.0, pistonVel);
182
183            // end of critical section
184            pLock.unlock();
185
186            // reset for next cycle
187            pistoncollisions = 0;
188            mv = 0.0;
189
190            // reset stop watch for next cycle
191            lastUpdate = std::chrono::system_clock::now();
192
193
194        } // eof cycle computations
195
196        //sleep at every iteration to reduce CPU usage
197        std::this_thread::sleep_for(std::chrono::milliseconds(1));
198
199    } // eof while loop
200
201
202    t1.join(); // it will close because it is monitoring the finish flag
203
204 }
```

Main.cpp

```cpp
1    #include <iostream>
2    #include <iomanip>
3    #include <fstream>
4    #include <string>
5    #include <thread>
6    #include <vector>
7    #include <array>
8    #include <random>
9    #include <time.h>
10   #include <vector>
11   #include <SDL.h>
12
13   #include "Ball.h"
14   #include "Wall.h"
15   #include "Piston.h"
16   #include "Globals.h"
17
18
19   // The window we will be rendering to
20   std::shared_ptr<SDL_Window> gWindow = nullptr;
21
22   // The window renderer
23   std::shared_ptr<SDL_Renderer> gRenderer = nullptr;
24
25   // Start up SDL and create window
26   bool initRenderer();
27
28   // Free media and shut down SDL
29   void closeRenderer();
30
31   // Draw circle using midpoint circle algorithm
32   void drawCircle(std::shared_ptr<SDL_Renderer> gRenderer,
33                   int32_t centreX, int32_t centreY, int32_t radius);
34
35   // Load parameters from a file
36   bool chooseSimulations();
37   bool loadParametersFromFile();
38   void printParameters();
39
40   // Create objects;
41   void createObjects(std::vector<std::shared_ptr<Wall>>& walls,
42                   std::shared_ptr<Wall>& piston, std::shared_ptr<Wall>& bottom,
43                   std::vector<std::shared_ptr<Ball>>& balls);
44
45   // Render objects
46   void renderBall(std::shared_ptr<Ball> ball);
47   void renderWalls(std::vector<std::shared_ptr<Wall>> walls);
48
49
```

```cpp
50    /* Main function */
51    int main(int argc, char* args[]) // needs argc and args[] for the SDL
52    {
53
54        // Simulation objects
55        std::vector<std::shared_ptr<Wall>> walls;
56        std::shared_ptr<Wall> piston;
57        std::shared_ptr<Wall> bottom;
58        std::vector<std::shared_ptr<Ball>> balls;
59
60
61        // Choose simulations
62        if (!chooseSimulations())
63            return 0;
64
65        // set min value for "e"
66        //if (coef_rest < 1e-6) {
67        //    coef_rest = 1e-6;
68        //}
69
70        // create the objects
71        createObjects(walls, piston, bottom, balls);
72
73        if (balls.size() >= 1 && is_testing > 0) {
74            // set for testing
75            balls.at(0)->setSpecificDirection(ball0_speed, ball0_vel_angle);
76            if (ball0_x != -1) {
77                double x, y;
78                balls.at(0)->getPosition(x, y);
79                balls.at(0)->setPosition(ball0_x, y);
80            }
81            if (ball0_y != -1) {
82                double x, y;
83                balls.at(0)->getPosition(x, y);
84                balls.at(0)->setPosition(x, ball0_y);
85            }
86            if (ball0_radius != -1) {
87                balls.at(0)->setRadius(ball0_radius);
88            }
89            if (ball0_mass != -1) {
90                balls.at(0)->setMass(ball0_mass);
91            }
92        }
93
94
95        if (balls.size() >= 2 && is_testing > 0) {
96            // set for testing
97            balls.at(1)->setSpecificDirection(ball1_speed, ball1_vel_angle);
98            if (ball1_x != -1) {
99                double x, y;
100                balls.at(1)->getPosition(x, y);
101                balls.at(1)->setPosition(ball1_x, y);
102            }
```

```
103        if (ball1_y != -1) {
104            double x, y;
105            balls.at(1)->getPosition(x, y);
106            balls.at(1)->setPosition(x, ball1_y);
107        }
108        if (ball1_radius != -1) {
109            balls.at(1)->setRadius(ball1_radius);
110        }
111        if (ball1_mass != -1) {
112            balls.at(1)->setMass(ball1_mass);
113        }
114    }
115
116    // msg for stopping the threads
117    bool finish = false;
118
119    // process piston dynamics
120    std::thread t1(processPiston, piston, bottom, std::ref(balls), std::ref(finish));
121
122    // Start up SDL and create window
123    if (!initRenderer())
124    {
125        std::cout << "Failed to initialize!" << std::endl;
126    }
127    else
128    {
129        // wait before starting
130        std::this_thread::sleep_for(std::chrono::milliseconds(100));
131
132        // simulate
133        for (auto ball : balls)
134        {
135            ball->simulate();
136        }
137
138        // initialize variables
139        bool quit = false; // loop flag
140        int tempKey = 0;
141
142        // Main loop
143        while (!quit)
144        {
145
146            SDL_Event e; // Event handler
147
148            // Handle keycylinder events on queue
149            while (SDL_PollEvent(&e) != 0)
150            {
151                // User requests quit
152                if (e.type == SDL_QUIT)
153                {
154                    quit = true;
155                }
```

```
156
157                     // adjust temp at bottom
158                     if (e.type == SDL_KEYDOWN && e.key.repeat == 0)
159                     {
160                         switch (e.key.keysym.sym)
161                         {
162                         case SDLK_LEFT:
163                             tempKey = -1;
164                             break;
165                         case SDLK_RIGHT:
166                             tempKey = +1;
167                             break;
168                         default:
169                             break;
170                         }
171                     }
172
173                     if (e.type == SDL_KEYUP && e.key.repeat == 0)
174                     {
175                         switch (e.key.keysym.sym)
176                         {
177                         case SDLK_LEFT:
178                             if(tempKey < 0)
179                                 tempKey = 0;
180                             break;
181                         case SDLK_RIGHT:
182                             if(tempKey > 0)
183                                 tempKey = 0;
184                             break;
185                         default:
186                             break;
187                         }
188                     }
189
190                 }
191
192             // update temp
193             if (tempKey == +1) {
194                 double temp = bottom->getHeat();
195                 if (temp < bottom_temp_max) {
196                     temp++;
197                     bottom->setHeat(temp);
198                 }
199             }
200             if (tempKey == -1) {
201                 double temp = bottom->getHeat();
202                 if (temp > bottom_temp_min) {
203                     temp--;
204                     bottom->setHeat(temp);
205                 }
206             }
207
208             // Clear screen
```

```cpp
209            if (background_color == 1) {
210                SDL_SetRenderDrawColor(gRenderer.get(), 0xFF, 0xFF, 0xFF, 0xFF);
211            }
212            else {
213                SDL_SetRenderDrawColor(gRenderer.get(), 0x00, 0x00, 0x00, 0xFF);
214            }
215            SDL_RenderClear(gRenderer.get());
216
217            // Render ball
218            for (auto ball : balls)
219            {
220                renderBall(ball);
221            }
222
223            // Render walls
224            renderWalls(walls);
225
226            // Update screen
227            SDL_RenderPresent(gRenderer.get());
228
229        } // eof main loop
230
231
232        // ask ball:simulate to terminate
233        for (auto ball : balls) {
234            ball->setShutdown();
235        }
236
237    }
238
239    // close renderer
240    closeRenderer();
241
242    // wait for thread before returning
243    finish = true;
244    t1.join();
245
246    return 0;
247 }
248
249
250 void createObjects(std::vector<std::shared_ptr<Wall>>& walls,
251     std::shared_ptr<Wall>& piston, std::shared_ptr<Wall>& bottom,
252     std::vector<std::shared_ptr<Ball>>& balls)
253 {
254     // create walls
255     for (int nw = 0; nw < 5; nw++)
256     {
257         walls.push_back(std::make_shared<Wall>());
258     }
259
260     // lateral walls
261     walls.at(0)->setPosition(cylinder_center_position_x - cylinder_width / 2,
```

162

```
262         cylinder_center_position_y);
263     walls.at(0)->setSize(wall_width, cylinder_height + wall_width);
264     walls.at(0)->setWallType(WallType::lateral);
265
266     walls.at(1)->setPosition(cylinder_center_position_x + cylinder_width / 2,
267         cylinder_center_position_y);
268     walls.at(1)->setSize(wall_width, cylinder_height + wall_width);
269     walls.at(1)->setWallType(WallType::lateral);
270
271     // piston, cover and bottom walls
272     walls.at(2)->setPosition(cylinder_center_position_x,
273         cylinder_center_position_y - cylinder_height / 2);
274     walls.at(2)->setSize(cylinder_width - wall_width, wall_width);
275     walls.at(2)->setWallType(WallType::piston);
276
277     walls.at(3)->setPosition(cylinder_center_position_x,
278         cylinder_center_position_y + cylinder_height / 2);
279     walls.at(3)->setSize(cylinder_width - wall_width, wall_width);
280     walls.at(3)->setWallType(WallType::bottom);
281
282     // create reference to piston
283     piston = walls.at(2);
284     piston->setMass(piston_mass);
285
286     // create reference to bottom
287     bottom = walls.at(3);
288     bottom->setHeat(bottom_temp_min);
289
290     // create cells into the cylinder
291     int nCells = 0;          // calc number of cells
292
293     int nRows, nCols;
294     double totalArea, filedArea, percentFiled;
295
296     percentFiled = 0.0;
297     nRows = nCols = 0;
298
299
300     for (int nc = 1; nc <= nballs; nc++)
301     {
302         int nr = nballs / nc;
303         if (double(nc) * double(nr) < nballs) { nr += 1; }
304
305         totalArea = (screen_height * percent_height) *
306             (screen_width * percent_width);
307
308         if ((screen_width * percent_width) / nc >
309                 (screen_height * percent_height) / nr) {
310             filedArea = pow(((screen_height * percent_height) / nr) *
311                 0.50, 2.0) * 3.14 * nballs;
312         }
313         else {
314             filedArea = pow(((screen_width * percent_width) / nc) *
```

```
315            0.50, 2.0) * 3.14 * nballs;
316        }
317
318        if (filedArea/totalArea > percentFiled) {
319            percentFiled = filedArea / totalArea;
320            nRows = nr;
321            nCols = nc;
322            nCells = nCols * nRows;
323        }
324
325    }
326
327    struct Cell {
328        double x, y;
329    };
330
331    std::vector<Cell> places;
332    double inicX, inicY, aux;
333    walls.at(0)->getPosition(inicX, aux);
334    inicX += wall_width * 0.5;
335    walls.at(2)->getPosition(aux, inicY);
336    inicY += wall_width * 0.5;
337
338    for (int nc = 0; nc < nCells; nc++)
339    {
340        Cell cell;
341        cell.x = (inicX)+(nc % nCols) * ((cylinder_width - wall_width) / nCols) +
342            ((cylinder_width - wall_width) / nCols) / 2.0;
343        cell.y = (inicY)+(nc / nCols) * ((cylinder_height - wall_width) / nRows) +
344            ((cylinder_height - wall_width) / nRows) / 2.0;
345        places.push_back(cell);
346    }
347
348    // create balls at the cells
349    for (int nb = 0; nb < nballs; nb++)
350    {
351        balls.push_back(std::make_shared<Ball>());
352        balls.at(nb)->setPosition(places.at(nb).x, places.at(nb).y);
353
354        // prevent ball size overflow
355        if (nCols * 2.0 * ball_radius > cylinder_width * 0.98) {
356            balls.at(nb)->setRadius(cylinder_width * 0.98 / nCols / 2.0);
357        }
358        else {
359            balls.at(nb)->setRadius(ball_radius);
360        }
361
362        balls.at(nb)->setRandomDirection(ball_speed);
363        balls.at(nb)->setMass(ball_mass);
364        balls.at(nb)->setGravity(ball_gravity);
365        balls.at(nb)->setG(ball_G * G_mult);
366        balls.at(nb)->setGasMode((gas_mode > 0));
367        balls.at(nb)->setCoefRestitution(coef_rest);
```

```
368            }
369
370        // set the reference to other balls and walls into each ball
371        for (auto ball : balls)
372        {
373            ball->setBalls(balls);
374            ball->setWalls(walls);
375        }
376    }
377
378    bool initRenderer()
379    {
380        // Initialization flag
381        bool success = true;
382
383        // Initialize SDL
384        if (SDL_Init(SDL_INIT_VIDEO) < 0)
385        {
386            std::cout << "SDL could not initialize! SDL Error: " << SDL_GetError() <<
387                std::endl;
388            success = false;
389        }
390        else
391        {
392            // Create window
393            gWindow = std::shared_ptr<SDL_Window>
394                (SDL_CreateWindow("Elastic Collisions of Multiple Balls Simulation",
395                    SDL_WINDOWPOS_UNDEFINED, SDL_WINDOWPOS_UNDEFINED,
396                    int(screen_width * zoom_factor), int(screen_height * zoom_factor),
397                    SDL_WINDOW_SHOWN), SDL_DestroyWindow);
398            if (gWindow == nullptr)
399            {
400                std::cout << "Window could not be created! SDL Error: "<<SDL_GetError()<<
401                    std::endl;
402                success = false;
403            }
404            else
405            {
406                // Create vsynced renderer for window
407                gRenderer = std::shared_ptr<SDL_Renderer>
408                    (SDL_CreateRenderer(gWindow.get(),
409                        -1, SDL_RENDERER_ACCELERATED | SDL_RENDERER_PRESENTVSYNC),
410                        SDL_DestroyRenderer);
411                if (gRenderer == NULL) {
412                    std::cout << "Renderer could not be created! SDL Error: " <<
413                        SDL_GetError() << std::endl;
414                    success = false;
415                }
416                else
417                {
418                    // Initialize renderer color
419                    SDL_SetRenderDrawColor(gRenderer.get(), 0xFF, 0xFF, 0xFF, 0xFF);
420                }
```

```
421                  }
422
423          }
424
425      return success;
426  }
427
428  void closeRenderer() {
429      // Quit SDL subsystems
430      SDL_Quit();
431  }
432
433  void drawCircle(std::shared_ptr<SDL_Renderer> renderer,
434                  int32_t centreX, int32_t centreY, int32_t radius)
435  {
436      const int32_t diameter = (radius * 2);
437
438      int32_t x = (radius - 1);
439      int32_t y = 0;
440      int32_t tx = 1;
441      int32_t ty = 1;
442      int32_t error = (tx - diameter);
443
444      while (x >= y)
445      {
446          //  Each of the following renders an octant of the circle
447          SDL_RenderDrawPoint(renderer.get(), centreX + x, centreY - y);
448          SDL_RenderDrawPoint(renderer.get(), centreX + x, centreY + y);
449          SDL_RenderDrawPoint(renderer.get(), centreX - x, centreY - y);
450          SDL_RenderDrawPoint(renderer.get(), centreX - x, centreY + y);
451          SDL_RenderDrawPoint(renderer.get(), centreX + y, centreY - x);
452          SDL_RenderDrawPoint(renderer.get(), centreX + y, centreY + x);
453          SDL_RenderDrawPoint(renderer.get(), centreX - y, centreY - x);
454          SDL_RenderDrawPoint(renderer.get(), centreX - y, centreY + x);
455
456          if (error <= 0)
457          {
458              ++y;
459              error += ty;
460              ty += 2;
461          }
462
463          if (error > 0)
464          {
465              --x;
466              tx += 2;
467              error += (tx - diameter);
468          }
469      }
470  }
471
472  void renderBall(std::shared_ptr<Ball> ball)
473  {
```

```
474        double x, y, r;
475        ball->getPosition(x, y);
476        r = ball->getRadius();
477
478        x = x * zoom_factor;
479        y = y * zoom_factor;
480        r = r * zoom_factor;
481
482        if (r < 1) r = 1;   // prevent the no plotting of smaller balls
483
484        if (x < 0) return;
485
486        if (background_color != 1) {
487            SDL_SetRenderDrawColor(gRenderer.get(), 0xFF, 0xFF, 0xFF, 0xFF);
488        }
489        else {
490            SDL_SetRenderDrawColor(gRenderer.get(), 0x00, 0x00, 0x00, 0xFF);
491        }
492
493        drawCircle(gRenderer, (int32_t) x, (int32_t) y, (int32_t) r);
494
495    }
496
497    void renderWalls(std::vector<std::shared_ptr<Wall>> walls)
498    {
499        for (auto wall : walls) {
500
501            // set the rectangle
502            SDL_Rect rect;
503            double x, y, w, h;
504            wall->getPosition(x, y);
505            wall->getSize(w, h);
506
507            x = x * zoom_factor;
508            y = y * zoom_factor;
509            w = w * zoom_factor;
510            h = h * zoom_factor;
511
512            if (x < 0) continue;
513
514            rect.x = int (x - w / 2);
515            rect.y = int (y - h / 2);
516            rect.w = int (w);
517            rect.h = int (h);
518
519            switch (wall->getWallType())
520            {
521                case WallType::lateral:
522                    //SDL_SetRenderDrawColor(gRenderer.get(), 0x00, 0x00, 0x00, 0xFF);
523                    SDL_SetRenderDrawColor(gRenderer.get(), 0xAF, 0xAF, 0xAF, 0xFF);
524                    break;
525                case WallType::piston:
526                    SDL_SetRenderDrawColor(gRenderer.get(), 0x00, 0x00, 0xFF, 0xFF);
```

```
527                 break;
528             case WallType::bottom:
529                 double k = (wall->getHeat() - bottom_temp_min) /
530                     (bottom_temp_max + 0.001);
531                 double kMin = bottom_temp_min / (bottom_temp_max + 0.001);
532                 uint8_t red = uint8_t(0xFF * 0.60 + (0xFF * kMin + 0xFF * k) * 0.40);
533                 SDL_SetRenderDrawColor(gRenderer.get(), red, 0x00, 0x00, 0xFF);
534                 break;
535         }
536
537         SDL_RenderDrawRect(gRenderer.get(), &rect);
538     }
539 }
540
541
542 bool loadParametersFromFile()
543 {
544
545     struct Reading {
546         std::string name;
547         double value;
548     };
549
550     std::cout << "Loading parameters file...\n" << std::endl;
551     std::cout << "Please enter input file name: [Parameters.txt]";
552
553     std::string iname;
554     std::getline(std::cin, iname);
555
556     if (iname.empty()) {
557         iname = "Parameters.txt";
558     }
559
560     // the input stream
561     std::ifstream ist{ iname };
562
563     if (!ist)
564     {
565         std::cout << "\nCan't open input file " << iname << std::endl;
566         return false;
567     }
568
569     if (ist)
570     {
571         std::cout << "Reading the file " << iname << " ...\n" << std::endl;
572     }
573
574     // it will store the data
575     std::vector<Reading> parameters;
576
577     // reading from file
578     while (ist) {
579         std::string name{};
```

```cpp
580              double value{};
581              ist >> name >> value;
582              if (ist) {
583                  parameters.push_back(Reading{ name, value });
584              }
585          }
586
587      // test the data
588      if (parameters.size() != 36)
589          return false;
590
591      // load in memory
592      for (auto parameter : parameters)
593      {
594          if (parameter.name == "GAS_MODE") gas_mode = parameter.value;
595
596          if (parameter.name == "NBALLS") nballs = int(parameter.value);
597          if (parameter.name == "BALL_RADIUS") ball_radius = parameter.value;
598          if (parameter.name == "BALL_SPEED") ball_speed = parameter.value;
599          if (parameter.name == "BALL_MASS") ball_mass = parameter.value;
600          if (parameter.name == "BALL_GRAVITY") ball_gravity = parameter.value;
601          if (parameter.name == "BALL_G") ball_G = parameter.value;
602          if (parameter.name == "PUSH_PULL") push_pull = int(parameter.value);
603          if (parameter.name == "COEF_RESTITUTION") coef_rest = parameter.value;
604
605          if (parameter.name == "IS_TESTING") is_testing = int(parameter.value);
606          if (parameter.name == "BALL0_SPEED") ball0_speed = parameter.value;
607          if (parameter.name == "BALL0_VEL_ANGLE") ball0_vel_angle = parameter.value;
608
609          if (parameter.name == "BALL0_X") ball0_x = parameter.value;
610          if (parameter.name == "BALL0_Y") ball0_y = parameter.value;
611          if (parameter.name == "BALL0_RADIUS") ball0_radius = parameter.value;
612          if (parameter.name == "BALL0_MASS") ball0_mass = parameter.value;
613
614          if (parameter.name == "BALL0_TIME") ball0_time = parameter.value;
615          if (parameter.name == "BALL0_DELTA_SPEED") ball0_delta_speed=parameter.value;
616          if (parameter.name == "BALL0_DELTA_ANGLE") ball0_delta_angle=parameter.value;
617
618          if (parameter.name == "BALL1_SPEED") ball1_speed = parameter.value;
619          if (parameter.name == "BALL1_VEL_ANGLE") ball1_vel_angle = parameter.value;
620          if (parameter.name == "BALL1_X") ball1_x = parameter.value;
621          if (parameter.name == "BALL1_Y") ball1_y = parameter.value;
622          if (parameter.name == "BALL1_RADIUS") ball1_radius = parameter.value;
623          if (parameter.name == "BALL1_MASS") ball1_mass = parameter.value;
624
625          if (parameter.name == "PISTON_MASS") piston_mass = parameter.value;
626          if (parameter.name == "PISTON_GRAVITY") piston_gravity = parameter.value;
627
628          if (parameter.name == "BOTTOM_TEMP_MIN") bottom_temp_min = parameter.value;
629          if (parameter.name == "BOTTOM_TEMP_MAX") bottom_temp_max = parameter.value;
630
631          if (parameter.name == "BACKGROUND") background_color = int(parameter.value);
632
```

```
633        if (parameter.name == "SCREEN_WIDTH") screen_width = parameter.value;
634        if (parameter.name == "PERCENT_WIDTH") percent_width = parameter.value;
635
636        if (parameter.name == "SCREEN_HEIGHT") screen_height = parameter.value;
637        if (parameter.name == "PERCENT_HEIGHT") percent_height = parameter.value;
638
639        if (parameter.name == "WALL_WIDTH") wall_width = parameter.value;
640
641        if (parameter.name == "ZOOM_FACTOR") zoom_factor = parameter.value;
642
643        cylinder_center_position_x = screen_width / 2;
644        cylinder_center_position_y = screen_height / 2;
645        cylinder_width = screen_width * percent_width;
646        cylinder_height = screen_height * percent_height;
647
648    }
649
650    return true;
651 }
652
653 void printParameters()
654 {
655     std::cout << "GAS_MODE " << gas_mode << std::endl;
656
657     std::cout << "NBALLS " << nballs << std::endl;
658     std::cout << "BALL_RADIUS " << ball_radius << std::endl;
659     std::cout << "BALL_SPEED " << ball_speed << std::endl;
660     std::cout << "BALL_MASS " << ball_mass << std::endl;
661     std::cout << "BALL_GRAVITY " << ball_gravity << std::endl;
662     std::cout << "BALL_G " << ball_G << std::endl;
663     std::cout << "PUSH_PULL " << push_pull << std::endl;
664     std::cout << "COEF_RESTITUTION " << coef_rest << std::endl << std::endl;
665
666     std::cout << "IS_TESTING " << is_testing << std::endl;
667     std::cout << "BALL0_SPEED " << ball0_speed << std::endl;
668     std::cout << "BALL0_VEL_ANGLE " << ball0_vel_angle << std::endl;
669
670     std::cout << "BALL0_X " << ball0_x << std::endl;
671     std::cout << "BALL0_Y " << ball0_y << std::endl;
672     std::cout << "BALL0_RADIUS " << ball0_radius << std::endl;
673     std::cout << "BALL0_MASS " << ball0_mass << std::endl << std::endl;
674
675     std::cout << "BALL0_TIME " << ball0_time << std::endl;
676     std::cout << "BALL0_DELTA_SPEED " << ball0_delta_speed << std::endl;
677     std::cout << "BALL0_DELTA_ANGLE " << ball0_delta_angle << std::endl << std::endl;
678
679     std::cout << "BALL1_SPEED " << ball1_speed << std::endl;
680     std::cout << "BALL1_VEL_ANGLE " << ball1_vel_angle << std::endl;
681     std::cout << "BALL1_X " << ball1_x << std::endl;
682     std::cout << "BALL1_Y " << ball1_y << std::endl;
683     std::cout << "BALL1_RADIUS " << ball1_radius << std::endl;
684     std::cout << "BALL1_MASS " << ball1_mass << std::endl << std::endl;
685
```

```
686    std::cout << "PISTON_MASS " << piston_mass << std::endl;
687    std::cout << "PISTON_GRAVITY " << piston_gravity << std::endl << std::endl;
688
689    std::cout << "BOTTOM_TEMP_MIN " << bottom_temp_min << std::endl;
690    std::cout << "BOTTOM_TEMP_MAX " << bottom_temp_max << std::endl << std::endl;
691
692    std::cout << "BACKGROUND " << background_color << std::endl;
693
694    std::cout << "SCREEN_WIDTH " << screen_width << std::endl;
695    std::cout << "PERCENT_WIDTH " << percent_width << std::endl;
696
697    std::cout << "SCREEN_HEIGHT " << screen_height << std::endl;
698    std::cout << "PERCENT_HEIGHT " << percent_height << std::endl;
699
700    std::cout << "WALL_WIDTH " << wall_width << std::endl;
701
702    std::cout << "ZOOM_FACTOR " << zoom_factor << std::endl;
703
704  }
705
706
707  bool chooseSimulations()
708  {
709
710      std::cout << "Please, choose one example or read parameters from a file:" <<
711          std::endl;
712      std::cout << "[1] Three balls. (default)" << std::endl;
713      std::cout << "[2] One ball at rest. Piston with gravity." << std::endl;
714      std::cout << "[3] Eight balls at rest. Piston with gravity." << std::endl;
715      std::cout << "[4] Fifty balls (gas simulation approximation)." <<
716          " Piston with gravity." << std::endl;
717      std::cout << "[5] Planet and Satellite." << std::endl;
718      std::cout << "[6] A Fictional Universe." << std::endl;
719      std::cout << "[7] Load parameters from a file." << std::endl;
720
721      std::string input;
722      std::cout << "\nOption: ";
723      std::getline(std::cin, input);
724
725      int menuOption = 1;
726
727      if (!input.empty())
728      {
729          menuOption = stoi(input);
730      }
731
732      switch (menuOption)
733      {
734      case 1:
735          // Simulation mode
736          gas_mode = 0;
737          // Ball
738          nballs = 3;                    // 100 max approx
```

171

```
739        ball_radius = 20;           // max 0.5 * WALL_WIDTH approx
740        ball_speed = 60;            // pixels/s (SPPED < RADIUS * 200 max approx)
741        ball_mass = 0.1;            // 0.01 * piston_mass min approx
742        ball_gravity = 0;           // if zero, simulate gas
743        // Piston
744        piston_mass = 10.0;
745        piston_gravity = 0.0;       // if zero, piston stops
746        break;
747
748    case 2:
749        // Simulation mode
750        gas_mode = 0;
751        // Ball
752        nballs = 1;                 // 100 max approx
753        ball_radius = 20;           // max 0.5 * WALL_WIDTH approx
754        ball_speed = 0;             // pixels/s (SPPED < RADIUS * 200 max approx)
755        ball_mass = 0.2;            // 0.01 * piston_mass min approx
756        ball_gravity = 0;           // if zero, simulate gas
757        // Piston
758        piston_mass = 10.0;
759        piston_gravity = 10.0;      // if zero, piston stops
760        break;
761
762    case 3:
763        // Simulation mode
764        gas_mode = 0;
765        // Ball
766        nballs = 8;                 // 100 max approx
767        ball_radius = 8;            // max 0.5 * WALL_WIDTH approx
768        ball_speed = 0;             // pixels/s (SPPED < RADIUS * 200 max approx)
769        ball_mass = 0.2;            // 0.01 * piston_mass min approx
770        ball_gravity = 0;           // if zero, simulate gas
771        // Piston
772        piston_mass = 10.0;
773        piston_gravity = 10.0;      // if zero, piston stops
774        break;
775
776    case 4:
777        // Simulation mode
778        gas_mode = 1;
779        // Ball
780        nballs = 50;                // 100 max approx
781        ball_radius = 4;            // max 0.5 * WALL_WIDTH approx
782        ball_speed = 60;            // pixels/s (SPPED < RADIUS * 200 max approx)
783        ball_mass = 0.1;            // 0.01 * piston_mass min approx
784        ball_gravity = 0;           // if zero, simulate gas
785        // Piston
786        piston_mass = 10.0;
787        piston_gravity = 10.0;      // if zero, piston stops
788        std::cout << "\nPlease, click on cylinder and increase energy" <<
789            " with '>' right key." << std::endl;
790        break;
791
```

```
792     case 5:
793         gas_mode = 0;
794         nballs = 2;                 // 100 max approx
795         ball_radius = 8;            // max 0.5 * WALL_WIDTH approx
796         ball_G = 1.0;
797         push_pull = 1;
798         coef_rest = 1.0;
799
800         is_testing = 1;
801         ball0_speed = 100.0;
802         ball0_vel_angle = 0;
803         ball0_x = 600;
804         ball0_y = 100;
805         ball0_radius = -1;
806         ball0_mass = 1e-6;
807
808         ball0_delta_speed = 1e-6;   // for turning on the printing of orbit
809
810         ball1_speed = 0.0;
811         ball1_vel_angle = 0;
812         ball1_x = 600;
813         ball1_y = 600;
814         ball1_radius = 50;
815         ball1_mass = 50.0;
816
817         // Piston
818         piston_mass = 1e10;
819         piston_gravity = 0.0;   // if zero, piston stops
820
821         background_color = 1;
822         screen_width = 1200;
823         percent_width = 0.90;
824         screen_height = 1200;
825         percent_height = 0.90;
826         wall_width = 20;
827         zoom_factor = 0.50;
828         break;
829
830     case 6:
831         gas_mode = 0;
832         nballs = 63;                // 100 max approx
833         ball_radius = 5;            // max 0.5 * WALL_WIDTH approx
834         ball_speed = 0;
835         ball_mass = 3.0;
836         ball_gravity = 0.0;
837         ball_G = 1.0;
838         push_pull = 0;
839         coef_rest = 0.85;
840
841         is_testing = 0;
842
843         // Piston
844         piston_mass = 1e10;
```

```
845            piston_gravity = 0.0;    // if zero, piston stops
846
847            background_color = 0;
848            screen_width = 4200;
849            percent_width = 0.90;
850            screen_height = 2800;
851            percent_height = 0.90;
852            wall_width = 100;
853            zoom_factor = 0.30;
854            break;
855
856        case 7:
857            if (!loadParametersFromFile())
858            {
859                std::cout << "Can not load the parameters file." << std::endl;
860                std::cout << "Please, verify if the file is at same directory " <<
861                    "of the executable (.exe) " <<
862                    "and if it has all the parameters." << std::endl;
863                std::cout << "Continue with the default? [y]" << std::endl;
864                std::string tc;
865                std::getline(std::cin, tc);
866                if (tc.empty()) {
867                    tc = "y";
868                }
869                if (tc == "y")
870                {
871                    // Simulation mode
872                    gas_mode = 0;
873                    // Ball
874                    nballs = 3;              // 100 max approx
875                    ball_radius = 20;        // max 0.5 * WALL_WIDTH approx
876                    ball_speed = 60;         // pixels/s (SPPED < RADIUS * 200 max approx)
877                    ball_mass = 0.1;         // 0.01 * piston_mass min approx
878                    ball_gravity = 0;        // if zero, simulate gas
879                    // Piston
880                    piston_mass = 10.0;
881                    piston_gravity = 0.0;   // if zero, piston stops
882                    break;
883                }
884
885                return false;
886            }
887            break;
888
889        default:
890            // Simulation mode
891            gas_mode = 0;
892            // Ball
893            nballs = 3;              // 100 max approx
894            ball_radius = 20;        // max 0.5 * WALL_WIDTH approx
895            ball_speed = 60;         // pixels/s (SPPED < RADIUS * 200 max approx)
896            ball_mass = 0.1;         // 0.01 * piston_mass min approx
897            ball_gravity = 0;        // if zero, simulate gas
```

```
898        // Piston
899        piston_mass = 100.0;
900        piston_gravity = 0.0;      // if zero, piston stops
901        break;
902    }
903
904    cylinder_center_position_x = screen_width / 2;
905    cylinder_center_position_y = screen_height / 2;
906    cylinder_width = screen_width * percent_width;
907    cylinder_height = screen_height * percent_height;
908
909    std::cout << "\nPlease, verify the simulation parameters:\n" << std::endl;
910    printParameters();
911
912    std::cout << "\nPress enter to continue..." << std::endl;
913    std::cin.ignore();
914
915    return true;
916 }
```

Parameters.txt

This file will have 36 parameters, more than double the initial version (Appendix A). All of them must be present because the program verifies its integrity by making a simple test and counting the parameters.

```
 1   GAS_MODE  0
 2   NBALLS  3
 3   BALL_RADIUS  8
 4   BALL_SPEED  50
 5   BALL_MASS  1.0
 6   BALL_GRAVITY  0
 7   BALL_G 0
 8   PUSH_PULL 1
 9   COEF_RESTITUTION 1.0
10
11   IS_TESTING  0
12   BALL0_SPEED 0.0
13   BALL0_VEL_ANGLE  0
14   BALL0_X -1
15   BALL0_Y -1
16   BALL0_RADIUS -1
17   BALL0_MASS -1
18
19   BALL0_TIME 0
20   BALL0_DELTA_SPEED 0
21   BALL0_DELTA_ANGLE 0
22
23   BALL1_SPEED  0
24   BALL1_VEL_ANGLE  0
25   BALL1_X -1
26   BALL1_Y -1
27   BALL1_RADIUS -1
28   BALL1_MASS -1
29
30   PISTON_MASS  1e10
31   PISTON_GRAVITY  0.0
32
33   BOTTOM_TEMP_MIN  0.0
34   BOTTOM_TEMP_MAX  100.0
35
36   BACKGROUND 0
37   SCREEN_WIDTH 480
38   PERCENT_WIDTH 0.50
39   SCREEN_HEIGHT 480
40   PERCENT_HEIGHT 0.90
41   WALL_WIDTH 20
42   ZOOM_FACTOR 1.00
```

```
1   cmake_minimum_required (VERSION 3.5)
2
3   add_definitions(-std=c++17)
4
5   set(CXX_FLAGS, "-Wall")
6   set(CMAKE_CXX_FLAGS, "${CXX_FLAGS}")
7
8   project(MbcsProjectCmake)
9
10  set(CMAKE_MODULE_PATH ${CMAKE_MODULE_PATH} "${CMAKE_SOURCE_DIR}/cmake/")
11
12  find_package(SDL2 REQUIRED)
13  include_directories(${SDL2_INCLUDE_DIRS} src)
14
15  find_package(Threads)
16
17  add_executable(MbcsProjectCmake "src/Main.cpp" "src/CylinderObject.cpp"
18                  "src/Wall.cpp" "src/Ball.cpp" "src/Piston.cpp")
19  string(STRIP "${SDL2_LIBRARIES}" SDL2_LIBRARIES)
20  target_link_libraries(MbcsProjectCmake ${CMAKE_THREAD_LIBS_INIT} ${SDL2_LIBRARIES} )
```

Appendix C

Here are the improvements in the program in Appendix B. There will be changes in "Ball.h", "Ball.cpp", "Globals.h", "Main.cpp", and "Parameters.txt". Because of that, we will show only these files, with the improvements in bold and above the "DONE" comments.

Globals.h

```
1    #ifndef GLOBALS_H
2    #define GLOBALS_H
3
4    // Simulation mode
5    double gas_mode = 0;            // choose the mode of simulation
6                                    // "standard"(0) or "gas"(1)
7    // Ball
8    int nballs = 8;                 // 100 max approx
9    double ball_radius = 8;         // max 0.5 * WALL_WIDTH approx
10   double ball_speed = 0;          // pixels/s (SPPED < RADIUS * 200 max approx)
11   double ball_mass = 0.2;         // 0.01 * piston_mass min approx
12   double ball_gravity = 0;        // if zero, simulate gas
13   double ball_G = 0;              // gravitational constant
14   const double G_mult = 1e5;
15   int push_pull = 1;              // push-pull balls apart after collision
16   double coef_rest = 1.0;         // coef. restitution collision between balls
17
18   int is_testing = 0;             // choose the testing mode (1) or normal mode (0)
19   double ball0_speed = 10;        // in testing mode, set the first two balls
20   double ball0_vel_angle = 0;
21   double ball0_x = -1;
22   double ball0_y = -1;
23   double ball0_radius = -1;
24   double ball0_mass = -1;
25
26   double ball0_time = 0;          // will update the velocity after time
27   double ball0_delta_speed = 0;
28   double ball0_delta_angle = 0;
29
30   double ball1_speed = 10;
31   double ball1_vel_angle = -180;
32   double ball1_x = -1;
33   double ball1_y = -1;
34   double ball1_radius = -1;
35   double ball1_mass = -1;
36
37   // DONE: create a global control variable for "virus" simulation option
38   int is_virus_simulation = 0;        // normal mode (0) or "virus" simulation (1)
39
40   // DONE: create a variable that represents the intermediate stage
```

```
41    double inter_period = 7.0; // time in sec
42
43    // Piston
44    double piston_mass = 10.0;
45    double piston_gravity = 10.0;    // if zero, piston stops
46
47    // Bottom
48    double bottom_temp_min = 0.0;
49    double bottom_temp_max = 100.0;
50
51    // Background color (black:0 white:1)
52    int background_color = 1;
53
54    // Screen and wall width dimensions
55    double screen_width = 480;
56    double screen_height = 480;
57    double wall_width = 20;
58
59    // cylinder position and dimensions
60    double cylinder_center_position_x = screen_width / 2;
61    double cylinder_center_position_y = screen_height / 2;
62
63    double percent_width = 0.50;
64    double cylinder_width = screen_width * percent_width;
65
66    double percent_height = 0.80;
67    double cylinder_height = screen_height * percent_height;
68
69    double zoom_factor = 1.0;
70
71    #endif
```

Ball.h

```cpp
1   #ifndef BALL_H
2   #define BALL_H
3
4   #include <mutex>
5   #include <deque>
6   #include <condition_variable>
7   #include <ctime>
8
9   #include "CylinderObject.h"
10  #include "Wall.h"
11
12
13  // forward declarations to avoid including cycle
14  class Wall;
15
16  // This is a message queue class for sending messages between threads
17  template <typename T>
18  class MessageQueue
19  {
20  public:
21      T receive();
22      void send(T&& msg);
23      int getSize();
24
25  private:
26      std::mutex _mutex;
27      std::condition_variable _cond;
28      std::deque<T> _queue;
29  };
30
31  enum class CollisionType {
32      wallCollision,
33      bottomCollision,
34      pistonCollision,
35  };
36
37  struct CollisionData {
38      CollisionType type;
39      double velY;
40  };
41
42  class Ball : public CylinderObject, public std::enable_shared_from_this<Ball>
43  {
44  public:
45      // constructor / destructor
46      Ball();
47
48      // getters / setters
49      void setWalls(std::vector<std::shared_ptr<Wall>> walls) { _walls = walls; }
50      void setBalls(std::vector<std::shared_ptr<Ball>> balls) { _balls = balls; }
51
```

```cpp
52      void setRadius(double r) { _radius = r; }
53      double getRadius() { return _radius; }
54
55      // This method will set a direction, calculating Vx and Vy based on speed and angle
56      void setSpecificDirection(double speed, double angle);
57
58      // This method will choose a random direction for the ball
59      void setRandomDirection(double speed);
60
61      // Gravitational Acceleration
62      void setGravity(double ball_gravity) { _ball_gravity = ball_gravity;  }
63      double getGravity() { return _ball_gravity; }
64
65      // Gravitational Constant (multiplied by a factor G_mult)
66      void setG(double ball_G) { _coef_G = ball_G; }
67      double getG() { return _coef_G; }
68
69      // Flag to set the "gas" mode model (piston counts the collisions)
70      void setGasMode(bool gas_mode) { _gas_mode = gas_mode;  }
71
72      // Coefficient of Restitution (for inelastic collisions)
73      void setCoefRestitution(double coef_e) { _coef_e = coef_e; }
74      double getCoefRestitution() { return _coef_e; }
75
76      // DONE: Get "virus" simulation data (this operations need to be protected with mutex)
77      void setVirusStage(int stage);
78      int getVirusStage();
79      void setInfectionTime(std::time_t time);
80      std::time_t getInfectionTime();
81
82      // typical behaviour methods
83      bool dataIsAvailable();          // inform that there is a message from other thread
84      CollisionData receiveMsg();      // receive msg from other thread (msg stored in queue)
85      void simulate();                 // process ball movements
86      void setShutdown();              // set the flag to exit while-loop in simulate()
87
88      // miscellaneous
89      std::shared_ptr<Ball> get_shared_this() { return shared_from_this(); }
90      std::mutex ball_mutex;
91
92  private:
93      // typical behaviour methods
94      void play();
95      // check if has collided with a wall
96      bool checkWallCollision(double nextX, double nextY, std::shared_ptr<Wall> wall);
97      // check if has collided with another ball
98      bool checkBallCollision(double nextX, double nextY, std::shared_ptr<Ball> ball);
99      // receive direct message to shutdown (exit while-loop)
100     bool getShutdown();
101
102     // member attributes
103     double _radius;                  // ball radius
104     double _ball_gravity;            // gravity
105     double _coef_G;                  // gravitational constant
106     bool _gas_mode;                  // simulation mode
```

```cpp
107        double _coef_e;                      // restitution coefficient
108
109        // DONE: attributes to control "virus" stage, time from last collision
110        int _virus_stage;      // "virus" stage: 0:"uninfected"; 1:"intermediarie"; 2:"recovery"
111        std::time_t _infection_time;       // time at infection
112
113        std::vector<std::shared_ptr<Wall>> _walls;  // walls of cylinder on which ball is on
114        std::vector<std::shared_ptr<Ball>> _balls;  // balls of cylinder on which ball is on
115        MessageQueue<CollisionData> _msgQueue;      // msg queue for communications with main
116        bool _shutDown;                      // ask ball to end simulation
117    };
118
119    #endif
120
```

Ball.cpp

```cpp
1    #include <iostream>
2    #include <thread>
3    #include <future>
4    #include <memory>
5    #include <random>
6    #include <algorithm>
7    #include <cmath>
8    #include <array>
9    #include <iomanip>
10   #include <string>
11   #include <ctime>
12
13   #include "Ball.h"
14
15   // Variables defined at Globals.h
16   extern double cylinder_center_position_x;
17   extern double cylinder_width;
18   extern double cylinder_center_position_y;
19   extern double cylinder_height;
20   extern int push_pull;
21   extern int is_testing;
22   // DONE: reference the control variable for "virus" simulation
23   extern int is_virus_simulation;
24   // DONE: reference the intermediate stage period
25   extern double inter_period;
26   extern double ball0_time;
27   extern double ball0_delta_speed;
28   extern double ball0_delta_angle;
29
30
31   template <typename T>
32   T MessageQueue<T>::receive()
33   {
34
35       std::unique_lock<std::mutex> uLock(_mutex);    // needs unique_lock because the lock
36       // will be temporarily unlocked inside wait
37       _cond.wait(uLock, [this] { return !_queue.empty(); });    // enter the wait state,
38       // release the lock and resume if new data is available
39
40       T msg = std::move(_queue.back());
41       _queue.pop_back();
42
43       //std::cout << "Message " << msg  << " has been received from the Ball msg queue"
44       // << std::endl;
45
46       return msg;
47   }
48
49   template <typename T>
50   void MessageQueue<T>::send(T&& msg)
51   {
```

```
52
53        std::lock_guard<std::mutex> uLock(_mutex);
54
55        //std::cout << "Message " <<  msg << " has been sent to the Ball msg queue"
56        // << std::endl;
57
58        _queue.push_back(std::move(msg));
59        _cond.notify_one();
60
61   }
62
63   template <typename T>
64   int MessageQueue<T>::getSize()
65   {
66        std::lock_guard<std::mutex> uLock(_mutex);
67        return _queue.size();
68   }
69
70   // helper function declaration
71   double distanceToPoint(double x1, double y1, double x2, double y2);
72   bool squareCircleCollision(double x1, double y1, double w1, double h1,
73                              double x2, double y2, double r2);
74   bool circleCircleCollision(double x1, double y1, double r1,
75                              double x2, double y2, double r2);
76   void resolveCollision(double& posX, double& posY, double& velX, double& velY,
77                         double speed, double mass, double radius,
78                         double& otherX, double& otherY,
79                         double& otherVx, double& otherVy,
80                         double otherSpeed, double otherM, double otherR, bool isWall,
81                         double coef_e, double coef_G);
82
83   Ball::Ball()
84   {
85        _type = ObjectType::objectBall;
86        _radius = 0;
87        _velX = 0;
88        _velY = 0;
89        _speed = 0;
90        _shutDown = false;
91        _ball_gravity = 0;
92        _gas_mode = false;
93        _coef_e = 0;
94        _coef_G = 0;
95        // DONE: initialize variables of "virus" simulation
96        _virus_stage = 0;
97        _infection_time = NULL;
98   }
99
100  // DONE: set/get "virus" simulation data
101  void Ball::setVirusStage(int stage) {
102       std::lock_guard<std::mutex> lock(_mutex);
103       _virus_stage = stage;
104  }
105
106  int Ball::getVirusStage() {
```

```cpp
107        std::lock_guard<std::mutex> lock(_mutex);
108        return _virus_stage;
109    }
110
111    // DONE: set/get infection time
112    void Ball::setInfectionTime(std::time_t time) {
113        std::lock_guard<std::mutex> lock(_mutex);
114        _infection_time = time;
115    }
116
117    std::time_t Ball::getInfectionTime() {
118        std::lock_guard<std::mutex> lock(_mutex);
119        return _infection_time;
120    }
121
122    void Ball::setSpecificDirection(double speed, double angle)
123    {
124        // set velocity
125        double vx, vy;
126        double pi = acos(-1);
127        vx = speed * cos(angle * 2 * pi / 360);
128        vy = -speed * sin(angle * 2 * pi / 360);
129        setVelocity(vx, vy);
130    }
131
132    void Ball::setRandomDirection(double speed)
133    {
134        // pick angle at random and set direction of the ball
135        double angle;
136        std::random_device rd;
137        std::mt19937 generator(rd());
138        std::array<double, 5> intervals{ -60.0, 60.0, 120.0, 240.0, 360.0 };
139        std::array<double, 4> weights{ 1.0, 1.0, 1.0, 1.0 };
140        std::piecewise_constant_distribution<double>
141            distribution(intervals.begin(), intervals.end(), weights.begin());
142        angle = distribution(generator);
143
144        std::cout << "Angle " << angle << std::endl;
145
146        // set velocity
147        setSpecificDirection(speed, angle);
148    }
149
150    bool Ball::dataIsAvailable()
151    {
152        return (_msgQueue.getSize() > 0);
153    }
154
155    CollisionData Ball::receiveMsg()
156    {
157        return _msgQueue.receive();
158    }
159
160    bool Ball::getShutdown()
161    {
```

```cpp
162        return _shutDown;
163    }
164
165    void Ball::setShutdown()
166    {
167        _shutDown = true;
168    }
169
170    // implement the virtual function that will execute a member function into a thread
171    void Ball::simulate()
172    {
173        // Start a thread with the member function "play" and the object "this"
174        // Add the created thread into the _threads vector of parent class (using
175        // emplace_back which means move semantics)
176        _threads.emplace_back(std::thread(&Ball::play, this));
177    }
178
179    // function which is executed in athread
180    void Ball::play()
181    {
182
183        // print Ball id and thread id
184        std::unique_lock<std::mutex> uLock(mtxCout);
185        std::cout << "Ball::simulate Ball _id=" << getID() << "  thread id=" <<
186        std::this_thread::get_id() << std::endl;
187        uLock.unlock();
188
189        long count = 0;
190
191        // initialize variables
192
193        // define cycle duration (to update ball position and check cylinder)
194        int cycleDuration = 10;  // duration of a single simulation cycle in ms
195
196        // init stop watch
197        std::chrono::time_point<std::chrono::system_clock> lastUpdate, simBegin;
198        lastUpdate = std::chrono::system_clock::now();
199        simBegin = std::chrono::system_clock::now();
200
201        // infinite simulation loop
202        while (!getShutdown())
203        {
204            // compute time difference to stop watch (in ms)
205            auto timeSinceLastUpdate = std::chrono::duration_cast<std::chrono
206                ::milliseconds>(std::chrono::system_clock::now() -
207                    lastUpdate).count();
208
209            // if past cycle time, update position and check cylinder
210            if (timeSinceLastUpdate >= cycleDuration)
211            {
212
213                // reset stop watch for next cycle
214                lastUpdate = std::chrono::system_clock::now();
215
216                // calc next position
```

```
217        double velX, velY, nextX, nextY;
218        double posX, posY, dx, dy;
219        getVelocity(velX, velY);
220        getPosition(posX, posY);
221
222        dx = velX * (timeSinceLastUpdate / 1000.0); // dx = Vx * dt
223
224        // calc gravity acceleration effect
225        dy = velY * (timeSinceLastUpdate / 1000.0) +
226            0.5 * _ball_gravity * pow(timeSinceLastUpdate / 1000.0, 2.0);
227
228        double dVy = _ball_gravity * (timeSinceLastUpdate / 1000.0);  // dVy = Ay*dt
229
230
231        // calc gravitational/force field
232        // F = G * m1 * m2 / r^2
233        // Gf = G * m2 / r^2
234        int thisBallId = getID();
235
236        double Gf = 0.0;      // field
237        double Gfx = 0.0;
238        double Gfy = 0.0;
239        double coef_G = getG();
240        double dGVx = 0.0;
241        double dGVy = 0.0;
242
243        if (coef_G > 0 || coef_G < 0)
244        {
245            for (auto ball : _balls)
246            {
247                int otherBallId = ball->getID();
248                if (thisBallId != otherBallId)
249                {
250                    double otherX, otherY;
251                    ball->getPosition(otherX, otherY);
252
253                    double m2 = ball->getMass();
254                    double r = distanceToPoint(posX + dx/2, posY + dy/2,
255                        otherX, otherY);
256                    Gf = coef_G * m2 / (r * r);
257                    double angle = atan2(otherY - posY - dy/2, otherX - posX -dx/2);
258                    Gfx += Gf * cos(angle);
259                    Gfy += Gf * sin(angle);
260                }
261            }
262
263            // calc gravitational acceleration effect
264            dx += 0.5 * Gfx * pow(timeSinceLastUpdate / 1000.0, 2.0);
265            dy += 0.5 * Gfy * pow(timeSinceLastUpdate / 1000.0, 2.0);
266
267            dGVx = Gfx * (timeSinceLastUpdate / 1000.0);   // dV = A*dt
268            dGVy = Gfy * (timeSinceLastUpdate / 1000.0);
269        }
270
271        // update velocity before entering the collision
```

```cpp
272            velX += dGVx;
273            velY += dVy + dGVy;
274
275            // update delta_speed in ball0
276            if ( _id == _balls.at(0)->getID() &&
277                (std::chrono::duration_cast<std::chrono::milliseconds>
278                (std::chrono::system_clock::now() - simBegin).count() > ball0_time) &&
279                ball0_time != 0 && is_testing == 1) {
280                velX += ball0_delta_speed * cos(ball0_delta_angle * acos(-1) / 180);
281                velY += ball0_delta_speed * (-1.0) * sin(ball0_delta_angle *
282                    acos(-1) / 180);
283                ball0_time = 0;
284            }
285
286            setVelocity(velX, velY);
287
288            // print time to orbit
289            if (_id == _balls.at(0)->getID() &&
290                ball0_time != 0 && getSpeed() < 1.0 && is_testing == 1) {
291                auto time = std::chrono::duration_cast<std::chrono::milliseconds>
292                    (std::chrono::system_clock::now() - simBegin).count();
293                double x1, y1, x2, y2;
294                _balls.at(0)->getPosition(x1, y1);
295                _balls.at(1)->getPosition(x2, y2);
296                double orbit = distanceToPoint(x1, y1, x2, y2);
297                uLock.lock();
298                std::cout << "speed: " << getSpeed() << " time: " << time <<
299                    " orbit:" << std::setprecision(6) << orbit << std::endl;
300                uLock.unlock();
301            }
302
303            // next position
304            nextX = posX + dx;
305            nextY = posY + dy;
306
307            // check if ball has colided
308            bool hasCollided = false;
309
310            // process ball with wall collision
311            // m0*v0i + m1*v1i = m0*v0f + m1*v1f
312            // Ec0i + Ec1i >= Ec0f + Ec1f
313            for (auto wall : _walls) {
314
315                // process piston->ball collision (the piston moves in y axis):
316                if (wall->getWallType() == WallType::piston)
317                {
318                    // begin of piston critical section
319                    std::unique_lock<std::mutex> pLock(wall->wall_mutex);
320
321                    // if ball is inside the piston: flag the collision
322                    if (checkWallCollision(nextX, nextY, wall)) {
323
324                        hasCollided = true;
325
326                        double otherVx, otherVy;
```

```
327                    wall->getVelocity(otherVx, otherVy);
328                    double x, y, w, h;
329                    wall->getPosition(x, y);
330                    wall->getSize(w, h);
331
332                    double velCollisionGas = velY;
333
334                    double otherX, otherY;
335                    otherX = posX;   // like collision with ball at same x coordinate
336                    otherY = y;
337
338                    double speed = getSpeed();
339                    double otherSpeed = wall->getSpeed();
340
341                    double mass = _mass;
342                    double otherM = wall->getMass();
343
344                    // limit piston movement to the cylinder
345                    if (otherY <= (cylinder_center_position_y -
346                        cylinder_height * 0.5) * 1.001)
347                    {
348                        otherM = 1e100;
349
350                    }
351
352                    double radius = _radius;
353                    double otherR = h / 2;     // it is like a collision with a ball
354                    // at the same x coordinate, with r = h/2
355
356                    double coef_e = getCoefRestitution();
357
358                    resolveCollision(posX, posY, velX, velY,
359                                     speed, mass, radius,
360                                     otherX, otherY, otherVx, otherVy,
361                                     otherSpeed, otherM, otherR, false,
362                                     coef_e, coef_G);
363
364                    // Two models of simulation: in the gas mode, the piston is
365                    // processed in main
366                    if (!(_gas_mode))
367                    {
368                        // update positions and velocities
369                        wall->setVelocity(0, otherVy);
370                        wall->setPosition(x, otherY);
371
372                        setVelocity(velX, velY);
373                        setPosition(posX, posY);
374
375                    }
376                    else
377                    {
378                        // update ball position and velocity
379                        setVelocity(velX, velY);
380                        setPosition(posX, posY);
381
```

```
382                          // msg to main, to update piston:
383                          _msgQueue.send({ CollisionType::pistonCollision,
384                                          velCollisionGas - velY });
385                      }
386
387                  }
388
389              // end of piston critical section
390              pLock.unlock();
391
392              if (hasCollided) {
393                  break;
394              }
395
396          }
397
398          // process collision with laterals
399          if (wall->getWallType() == WallType::lateral)
400          {
401
402              // if there is a collision, change ball direction
403              if (checkWallCollision(nextX, nextY, wall)) {
404
405                  //std::cout << "ball with lateral collision" << std::endl;
406
407                  hasCollided = true;
408
409                  double otherVx, otherVy;   // wall
410                  otherVx = 0;
411                  otherVy = 0;
412                  double x, y, w, h;
413                  wall->getPosition(x, y);
414                  wall->getSize(w, h);
415
416                  double coef_e = getCoefRestitution();
417
418                  double otherX, otherY;
419                  otherX = x;   // like collision with ball at same x coordinate
420                  otherY = posY;
421
422                  double speed = getSpeed();
423                  double otherSpeed = 0;
424
425                  double mass = _mass;
426                  double otherM = 1e100;
427
428                  double radius = _radius;
429                  double otherR = w / 2;     // it is like a collision with a ball
430                  // at the same y coordinate, with r = w/2
431
432                  resolveCollision(posX, posY, velX, velY,
433                                   speed, mass, radius,
434                                   otherX, otherY, otherVx, otherVy,
435                                   otherSpeed, otherM, otherR, true,
436                                   coef_e, coef_G);
```

```
437
438                    // update velocity
439                    setVelocity(velX, velY);
440
441                    // update position
442                    setPosition(posX, posY);
443
444                    break;
445
446              }
447
448          }
449
450          // process collision with bottom
451          if (wall->getWallType() == WallType::bottom)
452          {
453
454              if (checkWallCollision(nextX, nextY, wall)) {
455
456                  //std::cout << "ball with bottom collision" << std::endl;
457
458                  hasCollided = true;
459
460                  double otherVx, otherVy;  // bottom
461                  otherVx = 0;
462                  otherVy = 0;
463                  double x, y, w, h;
464                  wall->getPosition(x, y);
465                  wall->getSize(w, h);
466
467                  double coef_e = getCoefRestitution();
468
469                  double otherX, otherY;
470                  otherX = posX;  // like collision with ball at same x coordinate
471                  otherY = y;
472
473                  double speed = getSpeed();
474                  double otherSpeed = 0;
475
476                  double mass = _mass;
477                  double otherM = 1e100;
478
479                  double radius = _radius;
480                  double otherR = h / 2;    // it is like a collision with a ball
481                  // at the same x coordinate, with r = h/2
482
483                  resolveCollision(posX, posY, velX, velY,
484                                   speed, mass, radius,
485                                   otherX, otherY, otherVx, otherVy,
486                                   otherSpeed, otherM, otherR, true,
487                                   coef_e, coef_G);
488
489                  // Adjust ball velocity to aprox temperature effect of bottom
490                  if (wall->getWallType() == WallType::bottom) {
491                      if (abs(velY) < 1.0 * wall->getHeat())
```

```
492                              {
493                                  velY = -1.0 * wall->getHeat();
494                              }
495                          }
496
497                          // update velocity
498                          setVelocity(velX, velY);
499                          // update position
500                          setPosition(posX, posY);
501
502                          break;
503
504                      }
505
506                  }
507
508              } // eof ball-wall collision
509
510
511              // process ball with ball collisions
512              // m0*v0i + m1*v1i = m0*v0f + m1*v1f
513              // Ec0i + Ec1i >= Ec0f + Ec1f
514              if (!hasCollided)
515              {
516                  int thisBallId = getID();
517                  for (auto ball : _balls)
518                  {
519
520                      int otherBallId = ball->getID();
521
522                      if (thisBallId != otherBallId &&
523                          checkBallCollision(nextX, nextY, ball))
524                      {
525                          //uLock.lock();
526                          //std::cout << "ball:" << thisBallId << " with ball:" <<
527                          //    otherBallId <<  " collision" << std::endl;
528                          //uLock.unlock();
529
530                          // if there is a collision, change ball direction
531                          // elastic collision
532
533                          hasCollided = true;
534
535                          // DONE: process the transmission
536                          if (is_virus_simulation == 1) {
537
538                              time_t timer;
539                              time(&timer);
540                              // transmission to other ball
541                              // if other ball is uninfected, turn infected (stage 1)
542                              if (ball->getVirusStage() == 0 && getVirusStage() == 1) {
543
544                                  ball->setVirusStage(1);
545                                  ball->setInfectionTime(timer);
546
```

192

```
547                         // transmission from other ball
548                         // if this ball is uninfected, turn infected (stage 1)
549                    } else if (getVirusStage()==0 && ball->getVirusStage() == 1) {
550
551                         setVirusStage(1);
552                         setInfectionTime(timer);
553
554                    }
555               }
556
557               double otherX, otherY;
558               ball->getPosition(otherX, otherY);
559
560               double otherVx, otherVy;
561               ball->getVelocity(otherVx, otherVy);
562
563               // approx. do not use all dGV (collide first)
564               velX = velX - 0.5 * dGVx;
565               velY = velY - 0.5 * dGVy;
566
567               double speed = sqrt(pow(velX, 2.0) + pow(velY, 2.0));
568               double otherSpeed = ball->getSpeed();
569
570               double mass = getMass();
571               double otherM = ball->getMass();
572
573               double radius = getRadius();
574               double otherR = ball->getRadius();
575
576               double coef_e = getCoefRestitution();
577
578
579               resolveCollision(posX, posY, velX, velY,
580                                speed, mass, radius,
581                                otherX, otherY, otherVx, otherVy,
582                                otherSpeed, otherM, otherR, false,
583                                coef_e, coef_G);
584
585               // update velocities
586               setVelocity(velX, velY);
587               ball->setVelocity(otherVx, otherVy);
588
589               // update positions
590               setPosition(posX, posY);
591               ball->setPosition(otherX, otherY);
592
593          }
594
595        }
596
597     } // eof new ball-ball collision
598
599
600     // if has not colided, just update position (velocity has been updated)
601     if (!hasCollided) {
```

```
602                     setPosition(nextX, nextY);
603                 }
604
605             } // eof cycle
606
607
608             // DONE: process recovery stage of "virus" simmulation
609             if (getVirusStage() == 1) {
610                 time_t timer;
611                 time(&timer);
612                 if (difftime(timer, getInfectionTime()) > inter_period) {
613                     setVirusStage(2);
614                 }
615             }
616
617
618             // sleep at every iteration to reduce CPU usage
619             std::this_thread::sleep_for(std::chrono::milliseconds(1));
620
621         } // eof simulation loop
622
623
624         // print Ball id and thread id
625         uLock.lock();
626         std::cout << "Ball::simulate closing Ball _id=" << getID() << "  thread id=" <<
627             std::this_thread::get_id() << std::endl;
628         uLock.unlock();
629     }
630
631 // Verify and process the collision of the ball with the cylinder walls
632 bool Ball::checkWallCollision(double nextX, double nextY, std::shared_ptr<Wall> wall)
633 {
634     double x, y, w, h;
635     bool collision = false;
636
637     wall->getPosition(x, y);
638     wall->getSize(w, h);
639     collision = squareCircleCollision(x, y, w, h, nextX, nextY, _radius);
640
641     return collision;
642 }
643
644 // Verify and process the collision of the ball with the cylinder walls
645 bool Ball::checkBallCollision(double nextX, double nextY, std::shared_ptr<Ball> ball)
646 {
647     double x, y, r;
648     bool collision = false;
649
650     ball->getPosition(x, y);
651     r = ball->getRadius();
652     collision = circleCircleCollision(nextX, nextY, _radius, x, y, r);
653
654     return collision;
655 }
656
```

```
657    // verify collision between square x1,y1,w1,h1 and circle x2,y2,r2
658    bool squareCircleCollision(double x1, double y1, double w1, double h1,
659                               double x2, double y2, double r2)
660    {
661        double closestX, closestY;
662        bool collision = false;
663
664        // find the closest x coordinate of the wall to the circle
665        if (x1 + w1 * 0.5 < x2 - r2) { closestX = x1 + w1 * 0.5; }
666        else if (x1 - w1 * 0.5 > x2 + r2) { closestX = x1 - w1 * 0.5; }
667        else { closestX = x2; }
668
669        // find the closest y coordinate of the wall to the circle
670        if (y1 + h1 * 0.5 < y2 - r2) { closestY = y1 + h1 * 0.5; }
671        else if (y1 - h1 * 0.5 > y2 + r2) { closestY = y1 - h1 * 0.5; }
672        else { closestY = y2; }
673
674        if (distanceToPoint(x2, y2, closestX, closestY) < (r2 - 1e-3)) {
675            collision = true;
676        }
677
678        return collision;
679    }
680
681    // verify collision between circle x1,y1,r1 and circle x2,y2,r2
682    bool circleCircleCollision(double x1, double y1, double r1,
683                               double x2, double y2, double r2)
684    {
685        double distance;
686        bool collision;
687
688        distance = distanceToPoint(x1, y1, x2, y2);
689        collision = (distance < (r1 + r2 - 1e-3));
690
691        return collision;
692    }
693
694    double distanceToPoint(double x1, double y1, double x2, double y2)
695    {
696        double distance;
697
698        distance = sqrt(pow(x1 - x2, 2.0) + pow(y1 - y2, 2.0));
699
700        return distance;
701    }
702
703    // resolve collision elastic
704    void resolveCollision(double& posX, double& posY, double& velX, double& velY,
705                          double speed, double mass, double radius,
706                          double& otherX, double& otherY, double& otherVx, double& otherVy,
707                          double otherSpeed, double otherM, double otherR, bool isWall,
708                          double coef_e, double coef_G)
709    {
710
711        if (mass == 0 || otherM == 0)
```

```
712         {
713             std::cout << "Error: mass is zero!" << std::endl;
714             return;
715         }
716
717         double angleCol = atan2(otherY - posY, otherX - posX);
718         double direction = atan2(velY, velX);
719         double otherDirection = atan2(otherVy, otherVx);
720
721         double new_xspeed = speed * cos(direction - angleCol);
722         double new_yspeed = speed * sin(direction - angleCol);
723
724         double new_xspeedOther = otherSpeed * cos(otherDirection - angleCol);
725         double new_yspeedOther = otherSpeed * sin(otherDirection - angleCol);
726
727         double final_xspeed = ((mass - coef_e * otherM) * new_xspeed +
728             (otherM + coef_e * otherM) * new_xspeedOther) / (mass + otherM);
729         double final_xspeedOther = ((mass + coef_e * mass) * new_xspeed +
730             (otherM - coef_e * mass) * new_xspeedOther) / (mass + otherM);
731         double final_yspeed = new_yspeed;
732         double final_yspeedOther = new_yspeedOther;
733
734         double cosAngle = cos(angleCol);
735         double sinAngle = sin(angleCol);
736
737         double newVelX, newVelY;
738         newVelX = cosAngle * final_xspeed - sinAngle * final_yspeed;
739         newVelY = sinAngle * final_xspeed + cosAngle * final_yspeed;
740
741         double newOtherVelX, newOtherVelY;
742         newOtherVelX = cosAngle * final_xspeedOther - sinAngle * final_yspeedOther;
743         newOtherVelY = sinAngle * final_xspeedOther + cosAngle * final_yspeedOther;
744
745         // get the minimum translation distance to push balls apart after intersecting
746         struct Position {
747             double x;
748             double y;
749             double length() {
750                 return sqrt(pow(x, 2.0) + pow(y, 2.0));
751             }
752         } pos1, pos2, posDiff, mtd;
753
754         pos1.x = posX;
755         pos1.y = posY;
756         pos2.x = otherX;
757         pos2.y = otherY;
758         posDiff.x = pos1.x - pos2.x;
759         posDiff.y = pos1.y - pos2.y;
760
761         double d = posDiff.length();
762         double k = (((radius + otherR) - d) / d);
763         mtd.x = posDiff.x * k;
764         mtd.y = posDiff.y * k;
765
766         double im = 1 / mass;
```

```
767        double imOther = 1 / otherM;
768
769        // push-pull them apart based off their mass, if the flag was set
770        if (push_pull == 1 ) {
771            pos1.x = pos1.x + mtd.x * (im / (im + imOther));
772            pos1.y = pos1.y + mtd.y * (im / (im + imOther));
773            pos2.x = pos2.x - mtd.x * (imOther / (im + imOther));
774            pos2.y = pos2.y - mtd.y * (imOther / (im + imOther));
775
776
777            // Process ball with wall collision generated by the pushing balls apart
778            if ((pos1.x + radius >= cylinder_center_position_x + cylinder_width / 2) ||
779                (pos1.x - radius <= cylinder_center_position_x - cylinder_width / 2))
780            {
781                newVelX = -1.0 * newVelX;
782            }
783
784            if ((pos1.y + radius >= cylinder_center_position_y + cylinder_height / 2) ||
785                (pos1.y - radius <= cylinder_center_position_y - cylinder_height / 2))
786            {
787                newVelY = -1.0 * newVelY;
788            }
789
790
791            // if other is a wall of the cylinder, do not process (is not valid)
792            if (((pos2.x + otherR >= cylinder_center_position_x + cylinder_width / 2) ||
793                (pos2.x - otherR <= cylinder_center_position_x - cylinder_width / 2)) &&
794                !isWall)
795            {
796                newOtherVelX = -1.0 * newOtherVelX;
797            }
798
799
800            // if other is a wall of the cylinder, do not process (is not valid)
801            if (((pos2.y + otherR >= cylinder_center_position_y + cylinder_height / 2) ||
802                (pos2.y - otherR <= cylinder_center_position_y - cylinder_height / 2)) &&
803                !isWall)
804            {
805                newOtherVelY = -1.0 * newOtherVelY;
806
807            }
808
809        }
810
811    velX = newVelX;
812    velY = newVelY;
813    posX = pos1.x;
814    posY = pos1.y;
815    otherVx = newOtherVelX;
816    otherVy = newOtherVelY;
817    otherX = pos2.x;
818    otherY = pos2.y;
819
820 }
```

```cpp
1    #include <iostream>
2    #include <iomanip>
3    #include <fstream>
4    #include <string>
5    #include <thread>
6    #include <vector>
7    #include <array>
8    #include <random>
9    #include <ctime>
10   #include <vector>
11   #include <SDL.h>
12
13   #include "Ball.h"
14   #include "Wall.h"
15   #include "Piston.h"
16   #include "Globals.h"
17
18
19   // The window we will be rendering to
20   std::shared_ptr<SDL_Window> gWindow = nullptr;
21
22   // The window renderer
23   std::shared_ptr<SDL_Renderer> gRenderer = nullptr;
24
25   // Starts up SDL and creates window
26   bool initRenderer();
27
28   // Free media and shut down SDL
29   void closeRenderer();
30
31   // Draw circle using midpoint circle algorithm
32   void drawCircle(std::shared_ptr<SDL_Renderer> gRenderer,
33                   int32_t centreX, int32_t centreY, int32_t radius);
34
35   // Load parameters from a file
36   bool chooseSimulations();
37   bool loadParametersFromFile();
38   void printParameters();
39
40   // Create objects;
41   void createObjects(std::vector<std::shared_ptr<Wall>>& walls,
42                      std::shared_ptr<Wall>& piston, std::shared_ptr<Wall>& bottom,
43                      std::vector<std::shared_ptr<Ball>>& balls);
44
45   // Render objects
46   void renderBall(std::shared_ptr<Ball> ball);
47   void renderWalls(std::vector<std::shared_ptr<Wall>> walls);
48
49
50   /* Main function */
51   int main(int argc, char* args[]) // needs argc and args[] for the SDL
```

```cpp
52     {
53
54         // Simulation objects
55         std::vector<std::shared_ptr<Wall>> walls;
56         std::shared_ptr<Wall> piston;
57         std::shared_ptr<Wall> bottom;
58         std::vector<std::shared_ptr<Ball>> balls;
59
60
61         // Choose simulations
62         if (!chooseSimulations())
63             return 0;
64
65         // set min value for "e"
66         //if (coef_rest < 1e-6) {
67         //    coef_rest = 1e-6;
68         //}
69
70         // create the objects
71         createObjects(walls, piston, bottom, balls);
72
73         if (balls.size() >= 1 && is_testing > 0) {
74             // set for testing
75             balls.at(0)->setSpecificDirection(ball0_speed, ball0_vel_angle);
76             if (ball0_x != -1) {
77                 double x, y;
78                 balls.at(0)->getPosition(x, y);
79                 balls.at(0)->setPosition(ball0_x, y);
80             }
81             if (ball0_y != -1) {
82                 double x, y;
83                 balls.at(0)->getPosition(x, y);
84                 balls.at(0)->setPosition(x, ball0_y);
85             }
86             if (ball0_radius != -1) {
87                 balls.at(0)->setRadius(ball0_radius);
88             }
89             if (ball0_mass != -1) {
90                 balls.at(0)->setMass(ball0_mass);
91             }
92         }
93
94
95         if (balls.size() >= 2 && is_testing > 0) {
96             // set for testing
97             balls.at(1)->setSpecificDirection(ball1_speed, ball1_vel_angle);
98             if (ball1_x != -1) {
99                 double x, y;
100                balls.at(1)->getPosition(x, y);
101                balls.at(1)->setPosition(ball1_x, y);
102            }
103            if (ball1_y != -1) {
104                double x, y;
105                balls.at(1)->getPosition(x, y);
106                balls.at(1)->setPosition(x, ball1_y);
```

```
107              }
108              if (ball1_radius != -1) {
109                  balls.at(1)->setRadius(ball1_radius);
110              }
111              if (ball1_mass != -1) {
112                  balls.at(1)->setMass(ball1_mass);
113              }
114          }
115
116          // DONE: Set the balls for "virus" simmulation
117          if (is_virus_simulation > 0) {
118              // set the first ball with the infected stage
119              balls.at(0)->setVirusStage(1);
120              // set the first ball with the time
121              time_t time_now;
122              time(&time_now);
123              balls.at(0)->setInfectionTime(time_now);
124          }
125
126          // msg for stopping the threads
127          bool finish = false;
128
129          // process piston dynamics
130          std::thread t1(processPiston, piston, bottom, std::ref(balls), std::ref(finish));
131
132          // Start up SDL and create window
133          if (!initRenderer())
134          {
135              std::cout << "Failed to initialize!" << std::endl;
136          }
137          else
138          {
139              // wait before starting
140              std::this_thread::sleep_for(std::chrono::milliseconds(100));
141
142              // simulate
143              for (auto ball : balls)
144              {
145                  ball->simulate();
146              }
147
148              // initialize variables
149              bool quit = false; // loop flag
150              int tempKey = 0;
151
152              // Main loop
153              while (!quit)
154              {
155
156                  SDL_Event e; // Event handler
157
158                  // Handle key cylinder events on queue
159                  while (SDL_PollEvent(&e) != 0)
160                  {
161                      // User requests quit
```

```
162            if (e.type == SDL_QUIT)
163            {
164                quit = true;
165            }
166
167            // adjust temp at bottom
168            if (e.type == SDL_KEYDOWN && e.key.repeat == 0)
169            {
170                switch (e.key.keysym.sym)
171                {
172                case SDLK_LEFT:
173                    tempKey = -1;
174                    break;
175                case SDLK_RIGHT:
176                    tempKey = +1;
177                    break;
178                default:
179                    break;
180                }
181            }
182
183            if (e.type == SDL_KEYUP && e.key.repeat == 0)
184            {
185                switch (e.key.keysym.sym)
186                {
187                case SDLK_LEFT:
188                    if(tempKey < 0)
189                        tempKey = 0;
190                    break;
191                case SDLK_RIGHT:
192                    if(tempKey > 0)
193                        tempKey = 0;
194                    break;
195                default:
196                    break;
197                }
198            }
199
200        }
201
202        // update temp
203        if (tempKey == +1) {
204            double temp = bottom->getHeat();
205            if (temp < bottom_temp_max) {
206                temp++;
207                bottom->setHeat(temp);
208            }
209        }
210        if (tempKey == -1) {
211            double temp = bottom->getHeat();
212            if (temp > bottom_temp_min) {
213                temp--;
214                bottom->setHeat(temp);
215            }
216        }
```

```
217
218                 // Clear screen
219                 if (background_color == 1) {
220                     SDL_SetRenderDrawColor(gRenderer.get(), 0xFF, 0xFF, 0xFF, 0xFF);
221                 }
222                 else {
223                     SDL_SetRenderDrawColor(gRenderer.get(), 0x00, 0x00, 0x00, 0xFF);
224                 }
225                 SDL_RenderClear(gRenderer.get());
226
227                 // Render ball
228                 for (auto ball : balls)
229                 {
230                     renderBall(ball);
231                 }
232
233                 // Render walls
234                 renderWalls(walls);
235
236                 // Update screen
237                 SDL_RenderPresent(gRenderer.get());
238
239             } // eof main loop
240
241
242             // ask ball:simulate to terminate
243             for (auto ball : balls) {
244                 ball->setShutdown();
245             }
246
247         }
248
249     // close renderer
250     closeRenderer();
251
252     // wait for thread before returning
253     finish = true;
254     t1.join();
255
256     return 0;
257 }
258
259
260 void createObjects(std::vector<std::shared_ptr<Wall>>& walls,
261     std::shared_ptr<Wall>& piston, std::shared_ptr<Wall>& bottom,
262     std::vector<std::shared_ptr<Ball>>& balls)
263 {
264     // create walls
265     for (int nw = 0; nw < 5; nw++)
266     {
267         walls.push_back(std::make_shared<Wall>());
268     }
269
270     // lateral walls
271     walls.at(0)->setPosition(cylinder_center_position_x - cylinder_width / 2,
```

```
272          cylinder_center_position_y);
273      walls.at(0)->setSize(wall_width, cylinder_height + wall_width);
274      walls.at(0)->setWallType(WallType::lateral);
275
276      walls.at(1)->setPosition(cylinder_center_position_x + cylinder_width / 2,
277          cylinder_center_position_y);
278      walls.at(1)->setSize(wall_width, cylinder_height + wall_width);
279      walls.at(1)->setWallType(WallType::lateral);
280
281      // piston, cover and bottom walls
282      walls.at(2)->setPosition(cylinder_center_position_x,
283          cylinder_center_position_y - cylinder_height / 2);
284      walls.at(2)->setSize(cylinder_width - wall_width, wall_width);
285      walls.at(2)->setWallType(WallType::piston);
286
287      walls.at(3)->setPosition(cylinder_center_position_x,
288          cylinder_center_position_y + cylinder_height / 2);
289      walls.at(3)->setSize(cylinder_width - wall_width, wall_width);
290      walls.at(3)->setWallType(WallType::bottom);
291
292      // create reference to piston
293      piston = walls.at(2);
294      piston->setMass(piston_mass);
295
296      // create reference to bottom
297      bottom = walls.at(3);
298      bottom->setHeat(bottom_temp_min);
299
300      // create cells into the cylinder
301      int nCells = 0;          // calc number of cells
302
303      int nRows, nCols;
304      double totalArea, filedArea, percentFiled;
305
306      percentFiled = 0.0;
307      nRows = nCols = 0;
308
309
310      for (int nc = 1; nc <= nballs; nc++)
311      {
312          int nr = nballs / nc;
313          if (double(nc) * double(nr) < nballs) { nr += 1; }
314
315          totalArea = (screen_height * percent_height) *
316              (screen_width * percent_width);
317
318          if ((screen_width * percent_width) / nc >
319                  (screen_height * percent_height) / nr) {
320              filedArea = pow(((screen_height * percent_height) / nr) *
321                  0.50, 2.0) * 3.14 * nballs;
322          }
323          else {
324              filedArea = pow(((screen_width * percent_width) / nc) *
325                  0.50, 2.0) * 3.14 * nballs;
326          }
```

```cpp
327
328            if (filedArea/totalArea > percentFiled) {
329                percentFiled = filedArea / totalArea;
330                nRows = nr;
331                nCols = nc;
332                nCells = nCols * nRows;
333            }
334
335        }
336
337        struct Cell {
338            double x, y;
339        };
340
341        std::vector<Cell> places;
342        double inicX, inicY, aux;
343        walls.at(0)->getPosition(inicX, aux);
344        inicX += wall_width * 0.5;
345        walls.at(2)->getPosition(aux, inicY);
346        inicY += wall_width * 0.5;
347
348        for (int nc = 0; nc < nCells; nc++)
349        {
350            Cell cell;
351            cell.x = (inicX)+(nc % nCols) * ((cylinder_width - wall_width) / nCols) +
352                ((cylinder_width - wall_width) / nCols) / 2.0;
353            cell.y = (inicY)+(nc / nCols) * ((cylinder_height - wall_width) / nRows) +
354                ((cylinder_height - wall_width) / nRows) / 2.0;
355            places.push_back(cell);
356        }
357
358        // create balls in the cells
359        for (int nb = 0; nb < nballs; nb++)
360        {
361            balls.push_back(std::make_shared<Ball>());
362            balls.at(nb)->setPosition(places.at(nb).x, places.at(nb).y);
363
364            // prevent ball size overflow
365            if (nCols * 2.0 * ball_radius > cylinder_width * 0.98) {
366                balls.at(nb)->setRadius(cylinder_width * 0.98 / nCols / 2.0);
367            }
368            else {
369                balls.at(nb)->setRadius(ball_radius);
370            }
371
372            balls.at(nb)->setRandomDirection(ball_speed);
373            balls.at(nb)->setMass(ball_mass);
374            balls.at(nb)->setGravity(ball_gravity);
375            balls.at(nb)->setG(ball_G * G_mult);
376            balls.at(nb)->setGasMode((gas_mode > 0));
377            balls.at(nb)->setCoefRestitution(coef_rest);
378        }
379
380        // set the reference to other balls and walls into each ball
381        for (auto ball : balls)
```

```
382        {
383            ball->setBalls(balls);
384            ball->setWalls(walls);
385        }
386    }
387
388    bool initRenderer()
389    {
390        // Initialization flag
391        bool success = true;
392
393        // Initialize SDL
394        if (SDL_Init(SDL_INIT_VIDEO) < 0)
395        {
396            std::cout << "SDL could not initialize! SDL Error: " << SDL_GetError() <<
397                std::endl;
398            success = false;
399        }
400        else
401        {
402            // Create window
403            gWindow = std::shared_ptr<SDL_Window>
404                (SDL_CreateWindow("Collisions of Multiple Balls Simulation",
405                    SDL_WINDOWPOS_UNDEFINED, SDL_WINDOWPOS_UNDEFINED,
406                    int(screen_width * zoom_factor), int(screen_height * zoom_factor),
407                    SDL_WINDOW_SHOWN), SDL_DestroyWindow);
408            if (gWindow == nullptr)
409            {
410                std::cout << "Window could not be created! SDL Error: " << SDL_GetError() <<
411                    std::endl;
412                success = false;
413            }
414            else
415            {
416                // Create vsynced renderer for window
417                gRenderer = std::shared_ptr<SDL_Renderer>
418                    (SDL_CreateRenderer(gWindow.get(),
419                        -1, SDL_RENDERER_ACCELERATED | SDL_RENDERER_PRESENTVSYNC),
420                        SDL_DestroyRenderer);
421                if (gRenderer == NULL) {
422                    std::cout << "Renderer could not be created! SDL Error: " <<
423                        SDL_GetError() << std::endl;
424                    success = false;
425                }
426                else
427                {
428                    // Initialize renderer color
429                    SDL_SetRenderDrawColor(gRenderer.get(), 0xFF, 0xFF, 0xFF, 0xFF);
430                }
431            }
432
433        }
434
435        return success;
436    }
```

```cpp
437
438    void closeRenderer() {
439        // Quit SDL subsystems
440        SDL_Quit();
441    }
442
443    void drawCircle(std::shared_ptr<SDL_Renderer> renderer,
444                    int32_t centreX, int32_t centreY, int32_t radius)
445    {
446        const int32_t diameter = (radius * 2);
447
448        int32_t x = (radius - 1);
449        int32_t y = 0;
450        int32_t tx = 1;
451        int32_t ty = 1;
452        int32_t error = (tx - diameter);
453
454        while (x >= y)
455        {
456            //  Each of the following renders an octant of the circle
457            SDL_RenderDrawPoint(renderer.get(), centreX + x, centreY - y);
458            SDL_RenderDrawPoint(renderer.get(), centreX + x, centreY + y);
459            SDL_RenderDrawPoint(renderer.get(), centreX - x, centreY - y);
460            SDL_RenderDrawPoint(renderer.get(), centreX - x, centreY + y);
461            SDL_RenderDrawPoint(renderer.get(), centreX + y, centreY - x);
462            SDL_RenderDrawPoint(renderer.get(), centreX + y, centreY + x);
463            SDL_RenderDrawPoint(renderer.get(), centreX - y, centreY - x);
464            SDL_RenderDrawPoint(renderer.get(), centreX - y, centreY + x);
465
466            if (error <= 0)
467            {
468                ++y;
469                error += ty;
470                ty += 2;
471            }
472
473            if (error > 0)
474            {
475                --x;
476                tx += 2;
477                error += (tx - diameter);
478            }
479        }
480    }
481
482    void renderBall(std::shared_ptr<Ball> ball)
483    {
484        double x, y, r;
485        int virus_stage;
486
487        ball->getPosition(x, y);
488        r = ball->getRadius();
489        virus_stage = ball->getVirusStage();
490
491        x = x * zoom_factor;
```

```
492        y = y * zoom_factor;
493        r = r * zoom_factor;
494
495        if (r < 1) r = 1;   // prevent the no plotting of smaller balls
496
497        if (x < 0) return;
498
499        // DONE: adjust colors according to "virus" stage
500        if (background_color != 1) {
501            if (virus_stage == 0) {
502                SDL_SetRenderDrawColor(gRenderer.get(), 0xFF, 0xFF, 0xFF, 0xFF);
503            }
504            else if (virus_stage == 1) {
505                SDL_SetRenderDrawColor(gRenderer.get(), 0xFF, 0x20, 0x20, 0xFF);
506            }
507            else if (virus_stage == 2) {
508                SDL_SetRenderDrawColor(gRenderer.get(), 0x20, 0xAB, 0x20, 0xFF);
509            }
510
511        }
512        else {
513            if (virus_stage == 0) {
514                SDL_SetRenderDrawColor(gRenderer.get(), 0x00, 0x00, 0x00, 0xFF);
515            }
516            else if (virus_stage == 1) {
517                SDL_SetRenderDrawColor(gRenderer.get(), 0xFF, 0x20, 0x20, 0xFF);
518            }
519            else if (virus_stage == 2) {
520                SDL_SetRenderDrawColor(gRenderer.get(), 0x20, 0xAB, 0x20, 0xFF);
521            }
522        }
523
524        drawCircle(gRenderer, (int32_t) x, (int32_t) y, (int32_t) r);
525
526    }
527
528    void renderWalls(std::vector<std::shared_ptr<Wall>> walls)
529    {
530        for (auto wall : walls) {
531
532            // set the rectangle
533            SDL_Rect rect;
534            double x, y, w, h;
535            wall->getPosition(x, y);
536            wall->getSize(w, h);
537
538            x = x * zoom_factor;
539            y = y * zoom_factor;
540            w = w * zoom_factor;
541            h = h * zoom_factor;
542
543            if (x < 0) continue;
544
545            rect.x = int (x - w / 2);
546            rect.y = int (y - h / 2);
```

```
547          rect.w = int (w);
548          rect.h = int (h);
549
550          switch (wall->getWallType())
551          {
552              case WallType::lateral:
553                  //SDL_SetRenderDrawColor(gRenderer.get(), 0x00, 0x00, 0x00, 0xFF);
554                  SDL_SetRenderDrawColor(gRenderer.get(), 0xAF, 0xAF, 0xAF, 0xFF);
555                  break;
556              case WallType::piston:
557                  SDL_SetRenderDrawColor(gRenderer.get(), 0x00, 0x00, 0xFF, 0xFF);
558                  break;
559              case WallType::bottom:
560                  double k = (wall->getHeat() - bottom_temp_min) /
561                      (bottom_temp_max + 0.001);
562                  double kMin = bottom_temp_min / (bottom_temp_max + 0.001);
563                  uint8_t red = uint8_t(0xFF * 0.60 + (0xFF * kMin + 0xFF * k) * 0.40);
564                  SDL_SetRenderDrawColor(gRenderer.get(), red, 0x00, 0x00, 0xFF);
565                  break;
566          }
567
568          SDL_RenderDrawRect(gRenderer.get(), &rect);
569      }
570  }
571
572
573  bool loadParametersFromFile()
574  {
575
576      struct Reading {
577          std::string name;
578          double value;
579      };
580
581      std::cout << "Loading parameters file...\n" << std::endl;
582      std::cout << "Please enter input file name: [Parameters.txt]";
583
584      std::string iname;
585      std::getline(std::cin, iname);
586
587      if (iname.empty()) {
588          iname = "Parameters.txt";
589      }
590
591      // the input stream
592      std::ifstream ist{ iname };
593
594      if (!ist)
595      {
596          std::cout << "\nCan't open input file " << iname << std::endl;
597          return false;
598      }
599
600      if (ist)
601      {
```

```cpp
602        std::cout << "Reading the file " << iname << " ...\n" << std::endl;
603    }
604
605    // it will store the data
606    std::vector<Reading> parameters;
607
608    // reading from file
609    while (ist) {
610        std::string name{};
611        double value{};
612        ist >> name >> value;
613        if (ist) {
614            parameters.push_back(Reading{ name, value });
615        }
616    }
617
618    // test the data
619    if (parameters.size() != 38)  // DONE: adjust the number
620        return false;
621
622    // load in memory
623    for (auto parameter : parameters)
624    {
625        if (parameter.name == "GAS_MODE") gas_mode = parameter.value;
626
627        if (parameter.name == "NBALLS") nballs = int(parameter.value);
628        if (parameter.name == "BALL_RADIUS") ball_radius = parameter.value;
629        if (parameter.name == "BALL_SPEED") ball_speed = parameter.value;
630        if (parameter.name == "BALL_MASS") ball_mass = parameter.value;
631        if (parameter.name == "BALL_GRAVITY") ball_gravity = parameter.value;
632        if (parameter.name == "BALL_G") ball_G = parameter.value;
633        if (parameter.name == "PUSH_PULL") push_pull = int(parameter.value);
634        if (parameter.name == "COEF_RESTITUTION") coef_rest = parameter.value;
635
636        if (parameter.name == "IS_TESTING") is_testing = int(parameter.value);
637        // DONE: load the is_virus_simulation global variable
638        if (parameter.name == "IS_VIRUS_SIMULATION") is_virus_simulation =
639            int(parameter.value);
640        // DONE: load the duration of intermediarie stage global variable
641        if (parameter.name == "INTER_PERIOD") inter_period = parameter.value;
642
643        if (parameter.name == "BALL0_SPEED") ball0_speed = parameter.value;
644        if (parameter.name == "BALL0_VEL_ANGLE") ball0_vel_angle = parameter.value;
645
646        if (parameter.name == "BALL0_X") ball0_x = parameter.value;
647        if (parameter.name == "BALL0_Y") ball0_y = parameter.value;
648        if (parameter.name == "BALL0_RADIUS") ball0_radius = parameter.value;
649        if (parameter.name == "BALL0_MASS") ball0_mass = parameter.value;
650
651        if (parameter.name == "BALL0_TIME") ball0_time = parameter.value;
652        if (parameter.name == "BALL0_DELTA_SPEED") ball0_delta_speed = parameter.value;
653        if (parameter.name == "BALL0_DELTA_ANGLE") ball0_delta_angle = parameter.value;
654
655        if (parameter.name == "BALL1_SPEED") ball1_speed = parameter.value;
656        if (parameter.name == "BALL1_VEL_ANGLE") ball1_vel_angle = parameter.value;
```

```cpp
657          if (parameter.name == "BALL1_X") ball1_x = parameter.value;
658          if (parameter.name == "BALL1_Y") ball1_y = parameter.value;
659          if (parameter.name == "BALL1_RADIUS") ball1_radius = parameter.value;
660          if (parameter.name == "BALL1_MASS") ball1_mass = parameter.value;
661
662          if (parameter.name == "PISTON_MASS") piston_mass = parameter.value;
663          if (parameter.name == "PISTON_GRAVITY") piston_gravity = parameter.value;
664
665          if (parameter.name == "BOTTOM_TEMP_MIN") bottom_temp_min = parameter.value;
666          if (parameter.name == "BOTTOM_TEMP_MAX") bottom_temp_max = parameter.value;
667
668          if (parameter.name == "BACKGROUND") background_color = int(parameter.value);
669
670          if (parameter.name == "SCREEN_WIDTH") screen_width = parameter.value;
671          if (parameter.name == "PERCENT_WIDTH") percent_width = parameter.value;
672
673          if (parameter.name == "SCREEN_HEIGHT") screen_height = parameter.value;
674          if (parameter.name == "PERCENT_HEIGHT") percent_height = parameter.value;
675
676          if (parameter.name == "WALL_WIDTH") wall_width = parameter.value;
677
678          if (parameter.name == "ZOOM_FACTOR") zoom_factor = parameter.value;
679
680          cylinder_center_position_x = screen_width / 2;
681          cylinder_center_position_y = screen_height / 2;
682          cylinder_width = screen_width * percent_width;
683          cylinder_height = screen_height * percent_height;
684
685      }
686
687      return true;
688  }
689
690  void printParameters()
691  {
692      std::cout << "GAS_MODE " << gas_mode << std::endl;
693
694      std::cout << "NBALLS " << nballs << std::endl;
695      std::cout << "BALL_RADIUS " << ball_radius << std::endl;
696      std::cout << "BALL_SPEED " << ball_speed << std::endl;
697      std::cout << "BALL_MASS " << ball_mass << std::endl;
698      std::cout << "BALL_GRAVITY " << ball_gravity << std::endl;
699      std::cout << "BALL_G " << ball_G << std::endl;
700      std::cout << "PUSH_PULL " << push_pull << std::endl;
701      std::cout << "COEF_RESTITUTION " << coef_rest << std::endl << std::endl;
702
703      std::cout << "IS_TESTING " << is_testing << std::endl;
704      // DONE: print the is_virus_simulation global variable
705      std::cout << "IS_VIRUS_SIMULATION " << is_virus_simulation << std::endl;
706      // DONE: print the duration of intermediarie stage global variable
707      std::cout << "INTER_PERIOD " << std::fixed << std::setprecision(1) << inter_period
708          << std::endl << std::endl << std::defaultfloat << std::setprecision(6);
709
710      std::cout << "BALL0_SPEED " << ball0_speed << std::endl;
711      std::cout << "BALL0_VEL_ANGLE " << ball0_vel_angle << std::endl;
```

```
712
713        std::cout << "BALL0_X " << ball0_x << std::endl;
714        std::cout << "BALL0_Y " << ball0_y << std::endl;
715        std::cout << "BALL0_RADIUS " << ball0_radius << std::endl;
716        std::cout << "BALL0_MASS " << ball0_mass << std::endl << std::endl;
717
718        std::cout << "BALL0_TIME " << ball0_time << std::endl;
719        std::cout << "BALL0_DELTA_SPEED " << ball0_delta_speed << std::endl;
720        std::cout << "BALL0_DELTA_ANGLE " << ball0_delta_angle << std::endl << std::endl;
721
722        std::cout << "BALL1_SPEED " << ball1_speed << std::endl;
723        std::cout << "BALL1_VEL_ANGLE " << ball1_vel_angle << std::endl;
724        std::cout << "BALL1_X " << ball1_x << std::endl;
725        std::cout << "BALL1_Y " << ball1_y << std::endl;
726        std::cout << "BALL1_RADIUS " << ball1_radius << std::endl;
727        std::cout << "BALL1_MASS " << ball1_mass << std::endl << std::endl;
728
729        std::cout << "PISTON_MASS " << piston_mass << std::endl;
730        std::cout << "PISTON_GRAVITY " << piston_gravity << std::endl << std::endl;
731
732        std::cout << "BOTTOM_TEMP_MIN " << bottom_temp_min << std::endl;
733        std::cout << "BOTTOM_TEMP_MAX " << bottom_temp_max << std::endl << std::endl;
734
735        std::cout << "BACKGROUND " << background_color << std::endl;
736
737        std::cout << "SCREEN_WIDTH " << screen_width << std::endl;
738        std::cout << "PERCENT_WIDTH " << percent_width << std::endl;
739
740        std::cout << "SCREEN_HEIGHT " << screen_height << std::endl;
741        std::cout << "PERCENT_HEIGHT " << percent_height << std::endl;
742
743        std::cout << "WALL_WIDTH " << wall_width << std::endl;
744
745        std::cout << "ZOOM_FACTOR " << zoom_factor << std::endl;
746
747    }
748
749
750    bool chooseSimulations()
751    {
752
753        // DONE: create option for a "virus" simmulation
754        std::cout << "Please, choose one example or read parameters from a file:" <<
755            std::endl;
756        std::cout << "[1] Three balls. (default)" << std::endl;
757        std::cout << "[2] One ball at rest. Piston with gravity." << std::endl;
758        std::cout << "[3] Eight balls at rest. Piston with gravity." << std::endl;
759        std::cout << "[4] Fifty balls (gas simulation approximation)." <<
760            " Piston with gravity." << std::endl;
761        std::cout << "[5] Planet and Satellite." << std::endl;
762        std::cout << "[6] A Fictional Universe." << std::endl;
763        std::cout << "[7] Five balls computer virus simulation (intermediate period 20s)."
764            << std::endl;
765        std::cout << "[8] Fifty balls computer virus simulation (intermediate period 7s)." <<
766    std::endl;
```

```cpp
767    std::cout << "[9] Fifty balls computer virus simulation (1/2 speed)." << std::endl;
768    std::cout << "[10] Load parameters from a file." << std::endl;
769
770    std::string input;
771    std::cout << "\nOption: ";
772    std::getline(std::cin, input);
773
774    int menuOption = 1;
775
776    if (!input.empty())
777    {
778        menuOption = stoi(input);
779    }
780
781    switch (menuOption)
782    {
783    case 1:
784        // Simulation mode
785        gas_mode = 0;
786
787        // Balls
788        nballs = 3;                  // 100 max approx
789        ball_radius = 20;            // max 0.5 * WALL_WIDTH approx
790        ball_speed = 60;             // pixels/s (SPPED < RADIUS * 200 max approx)
791        ball_mass = 0.1;             // 0.01 * piston_mass min approx
792        ball_gravity = 0;            // if zero, simulate gas
793
794        // Piston
795        piston_mass = 10.0;
796        piston_gravity = 0.0;        // if zero, piston stops
797        break;
798
799    case 2:
800        // Simulation mode
801        gas_mode = 0;
802        // Balls
803        nballs = 1;                  // 100 max approx
804        ball_radius = 20;            // max 0.5 * WALL_WIDTH approx
805        ball_speed = 0;              // pixels/s (SPPED < RADIUS * 200 max approx)
806        ball_mass = 0.2;             // 0.01 * piston_mass min approx
807        ball_gravity = 0;            // if zero, simulate gas
808
809        // Piston
810        piston_mass = 10.0;
811        piston_gravity = 10.0;       // if zero, piston stops
812        break;
813
814    case 3:
815        // Simulation mode
816        gas_mode = 0;
817
818        // Balls
819        nballs = 8;                  // 100 max approx
820        ball_radius = 8;             // max 0.5 * WALL_WIDTH approx
821        ball_speed = 0;              // pixels/s (SPPED < RADIUS * 200 max approx)
```

```
822        ball_mass = 0.2;              // 0.01 * piston_mass min approx
823        ball_gravity = 0;             // if zero, simulate gas
824
825        // Piston
826        piston_mass = 10.0;
827        piston_gravity = 10.0;    // if zero, piston stops
828        break;
829
830    case 4:
831        // Simulation mode
832        gas_mode = 1;
833
834        // Balls
835        nballs = 50;                  // 100 max approx
836        ball_radius = 4;              // max 0.5 * WALL_WIDTH approx
837        ball_speed = 60;              // pixels/s (SPPED < RADIUS * 200 max approx)
838        ball_mass = 0.1;              // 0.01 * piston_mass min approx
839        ball_gravity = 0;             // if zero, simulate gas
840
841        // Piston
842        piston_mass = 10.0;
843        piston_gravity = 10.0;    // if zero, piston stops
844        std::cout << "\nPlease, click on cylinder and increase energy" <<
845            " with '>' right key." << std::endl;
846        break;
847
848    case 5:
849        // Simulation mode
850        gas_mode = 0;
851        is_testing = 1;
852
853        // Balls
854        nballs = 2;                   // 100 max approx
855        ball_radius = 8;              // max 0.5 * WALL_WIDTH approx
856        ball_G = 1.0;
857        push_pull = 1;
858        coef_rest = 1.0;
859
860        ball0_speed = 100.0;
861        ball0_vel_angle = 0;
862        ball0_x = 600;
863        ball0_y = 100;
864        ball0_radius = -1;
865        ball0_mass = 1e-6;
866
867        ball0_delta_speed = 1e-6;    // for turning-on the printing of orbit
868
869        ball1_speed = 0.0;
870        ball1_vel_angle = 0;
871        ball1_x = 600;
872        ball1_y = 600;
873        ball1_radius = 50;
874        ball1_mass = 50.0;
875
876        // Piston
```

```
877         piston_mass = 1e10;
878         piston_gravity = 0.0;    // if zero, piston stops
879
880         // Screen
881         background_color = 1;
882         screen_width = 1200;
883         percent_width = 0.90;
884         screen_height = 1200;
885         percent_height = 0.90;
886         wall_width = 20;
887         zoom_factor = 0.50;
888         break;
889
890     case 6:
891         // Simulation mode
892         gas_mode = 0;
893         is_testing = 0;
894
895         // Balls
896         nballs = 63;                 // 100 max approx
897         ball_radius = 5;             // max 0.5 * WALL_WIDTH approx
898         ball_speed = 0;
899         ball_mass = 3.0;
900         ball_gravity = 0.0;
901         ball_G = 1.0;
902         push_pull = 0;
903         coef_rest = 0.85;
904
905         // Piston
906         piston_mass = 1e10;
907         piston_gravity = 0.0;    // if zero, piston stops
908
909         // Screen
910         background_color = 0;
911         screen_width = 4200;
912         percent_width = 0.90;
913         screen_height = 2800;
914         percent_height = 0.90;
915         wall_width = 100;
916         zoom_factor = 0.30;
917         break;
918
919     // DONE: create a small "virus" simulation for testing
920     case 7:
921         // Simulation mode
922         is_virus_simulation = 1;
923         inter_period = 20.0;
924         gas_mode = 0;
925
926         // Balls
927         nballs = 5;                  // 100 max approx
928         ball_radius = 20;            // max 0.5 * WALL_WIDTH approx
929         ball_speed = 60;             // pixels/s (SPPED < RADIUS * 200 max approx)
930         ball_mass = 0.1;             // 0.01 * piston_mass min approx
931         ball_gravity = 0;            // if zero, simulate gas
```

```
932
933              // Piston
934              piston_mass = 10.0;
935              piston_gravity = 0.0;      // if zero, piston stops
936
937              // Screen
938              screen_width = 480;
939              percent_width = 0.90;
940              screen_height = 480;
941              percent_height = 0.90;
942              wall_width = 20;
943              zoom_factor = 1.0;
944              break;
945
946      // DONE: create option for a "virus" simmulation
947      case 8:
948              // Simulation mode
949              is_virus_simulation = 1;
950              inter_period = 7.0;
951              gas_mode = 0;
952
953              // Balls
954              nballs = 50;               // 100 max approx
955              ball_radius = 4;           // max 0.5 * WALL_WIDTH approx
956              ball_speed = 60;           // pixels/s (SPPED < RADIUS * 200 max approx)
957              ball_mass = 0.1;           // 0.01 * piston_mass min approx
958              ball_gravity = 0;          // if zero, simulate gas
959
960              // Piston
961              piston_mass = 10.0;
962              piston_gravity = 0.0;      // if zero, piston stops
963
964              // Screen
965              screen_width = 480;
966              percent_width = 0.90;
967              screen_height = 480;
968              percent_height = 0.90;
969              wall_width = 20;
970              zoom_factor = 1.0;
971              break;
972
973      // DONE: create option for a "virus" simmulation
974      case 9:
975              // Simulation mode
976              is_virus_simulation = 1;
977              inter_period = 7.0;
978              gas_mode = 0;
979
980              // Balls
981              nballs = 50;               // 100 max approx
982              ball_radius = 4;           // max 0.5 * WALL_WIDTH approx
983              ball_speed = 30;           // pixels/s (SPPED < RADIUS * 200 max approx)
984              ball_mass = 0.1;           // 0.01 * piston_mass min approx
985              ball_gravity = 0;          // if zero, simulate gas
986
```

```cpp
987              // Piston
988              piston_mass = 10.0;
989              piston_gravity = 0.0;     // if zero, piston stops
990
991              // Screen
992              screen_width = 480;
993              percent_width = 0.90;
994              screen_height = 480;
995              percent_height = 0.90;
996              wall_width = 20;
997              zoom_factor = 1.0;
998              break;
999
1000         case 10:
1001             if (!loadParametersFromFile())
1002             {
1003                 std::cout << "Can not load the parameters file." << std::endl;
1004                 std::cout << "Please, verify if the file is at same directory " <<
1005                     "of the executable (.exe) " <<
1006                     "and if it has all the parameters." << std::endl;
1007                 std::cout << "Continue with the default? [y]" << std::endl;
1008                 std::string tc;
1009                 std::getline(std::cin, tc);
1010                 if (tc.empty()) {
1011                     tc = "y";
1012                 }
1013                 if (tc == "y")
1014                 {
1015                     // Simulation mode
1016                     gas_mode = 0;
1017                     // Ball
1018                     nballs = 3;            // 100 max approx
1019                     ball_radius = 20;      // max 0.5 * WALL_WIDTH approx
1020                     ball_speed = 60;       // pixels/s (SPPED < RADIUS * 200 max approx)
1021                     ball_mass = 0.1;       // 0.01 * piston_mass min approx
1022                     ball_gravity = 0;      // if zero, simulate gas
1023                     // Piston
1024                     piston_mass = 10.0;
1025                     piston_gravity = 0.0;  // if zero, piston stops
1026                     break;
1027                 }
1028
1029                 return false;
1030             }
1031             break;
1032
1033         default:
1034             // Simulation mode
1035             gas_mode = 0;
1036             // Ball
1037             nballs = 3;            // 100 max approx
1038             ball_radius = 20;      // max 0.5 * WALL_WIDTH approx
1039             ball_speed = 60;       // pixels/s (SPPED < RADIUS * 200 max approx)
1040             ball_mass = 0.1;       // 0.01 * piston_mass min approx
1041             ball_gravity = 0;      // if zero, simulate gas
```

```
1042            // Piston
1043            piston_mass = 100.0;
1044            piston_gravity = 0.0;      // if zero, piston stops
1045            break;
1046        }
1047
1048        cylinder_center_position_x = screen_width / 2;
1049        cylinder_center_position_y = screen_height / 2;
1050        cylinder_width = screen_width * percent_width;
1051        cylinder_height = screen_height * percent_height;
1052
1053        std::cout << "\nPlease, verify the simulation parameters:\n" << std::endl;
1054        printParameters();
1055
1056        std::cout << "\nPress enter to continue..." << std::endl;
1057        std::cin.ignore();
1058
1059        return true;
1060    }
1061
```

This file will have 38 parameters, two more than Appendix B (see lines 12-13). All of them must be present because the program verifies its integrity by making a simple test and counting the parameters.

```
1    GAS_MODE  0
2    NBALLS  3
3    BALL_RADIUS  8
4    BALL_SPEED  50
5    BALL_MASS  1.0
6    BALL_GRAVITY  0
7    BALL_G 0
8    PUSH_PULL 1
9    COEF_RESTITUTION 1.0
10
11   IS_TESTING  1
12   IS_VIRUS_SIMULATION 0
13   INTER_PERIOD 7.0
14
15   BALL0_SPEED 0.0
16   BALL0_VEL_ANGLE   0
17   BALL0_X -1
18   BALL0_Y -1
19   BALL0_RADIUS -1
20   BALL0_MASS -1
21
22   BALL0_TIME 0
23   BALL0_DELTA_SPEED 0
24   BALL0_DELTA_ANGLE 0
25
26   BALL1_SPEED   0
27   BALL1_VEL_ANGLE   0
28   BALL1_X -1
29   BALL1_Y -1
30   BALL1_RADIUS -1
31   BALL1_MASS -1
32
33   PISTON_MASS  1e10
34   PISTON_GRAVITY  0.0
35
36   BOTTOM_TEMP_MIN  0.0
37   BOTTOM_TEMP_MAX  100.0
38
39   BACKGROUND 0
40   SCREEN_WIDTH 480
41   PERCENT_WIDTH 0.50
42   SCREEN_HEIGHT 480
43   PERCENT_HEIGHT 0.90
```

```
44    WALL_WIDTH 20
45    ZOOM_FACTOR 1.00
```

CPSIA information can be obtained
at www.ICGtesting.com
Printed in the USA
BVHW021804140722
642153BV00008B/543